Printing
LAYOUT
and
Design

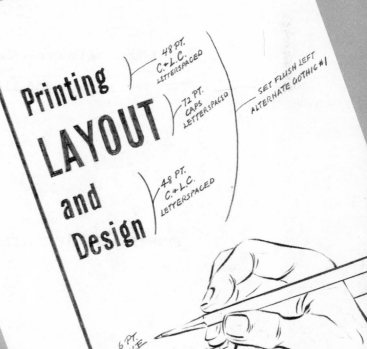

DELMAR PUBLISHERS, Inc.
ALBANY, NEW YORK

Preface

COURSE
OBJECTIVES   PRINTING LAYOUT AND DESIGN is tested instructional material designed to provide a knowledge of the basic principles of printing design and to develop skill in their application. While prepared specifically to meet the needs of students and apprentices, this material should serve the needs of anyone who requires a sound basic background in the layout and design of printing.

THE SCOPE   The content for this instructional material was determined under the direction of the Connecticut Curriculum Committee for the Printing Trades. Mr. Kenneth Orr, Instructor of Printing Layout and Design, Hartford Regional Technical School, developed the original material. After testing it in actual class use and revising it as good instruction required, Mr. Orr refined the material to its present form.

ORGANIZATION
AND FORMAT   The material is organized in the unit-pattern format. Each unit presents a principle of design and with abundant illustrations explains both good and poor practice in its application. The unit concludes with an assignment in layout which requires the student to apply the principle discussed. Each layout becomes succeedingly more difficult as the trainee progresses and necessitates the recall of principles previously covered in the text. To assure mastery of the content, periodic Review Tests are included. Each Section except the fifth concludes with a Review covering the entire section. Upon concluding Section V, jobs from Section VI, APPLICATIONS, may be selected not only as a review of the section, but as an application of the total course content. The series of jobs in Section VI provides the opportunity of designing the layout and carrying it through to completion. Thus, related theory is correlated with shop practice and the trainee becomes more familiar with the actual work (setting type, mounting, pulling proofs, etc.) which his layout calls for.

SUGGESTED
MATERIALS   Each student should have a tracing paper layout pad (11″ × 14″ is a convenient size), pencils, line gauge, and gum eraser. The instructor should have available colored pencils or pastels, and a supply of type specimen sheets. These sheets may be secured from local typesetting companies or by writing to the American Type Founders, Elizabeth, New Jersey. The student should be supplied with a variety of illustrations to be traced into the cuts when executing the layouts. Such illustrations may be clipped from national magazines and mounted on 4″ × 6″ bristol board for student use.

*   *   *   *

ACKNOWLEDGMENTS   To Mr. Kenneth Orr, Hartford Regional Technical School, Hartford, Connecticut must entire credit be given for the preparation and illustration of this material. Special recognition is made for the leadership given in both the initial and final stages of planning by Richard W. Howes, Assistant Director, Bureau of Vocational Education, Connecticut State Education Department; to Anna C. Moore, Consultant and Joseph Nerden, Chief, Trade and Industrial Education; and to Emmet A. O'Brien, Director of the Division of Vocational Education, for helpful cooperation.

Albany, New York
October 1955   The Editor

Contents

Section I

Principles of Conventional Layout

Section II

Principles of Modern Layout

Section III

Type

Section IV

Color

Section V

Special Layout Considerations

Section VI

Applications

Jobs 1 - 16 are a series of problems designed to give practice in carrying typical layouts through to completion.

Principles of Conventional Layout

Unit 1   INTRODUCTION TO PRINTING LAYOUT

THE LAYOUT MAN

Large printing plants have men who specialize in designing and arranging copy for printing. This type of work is called layout work and those engaged in doing this are called layout men. The layout man works on tracing paper and plans the printing just as an architect makes the plans and blue prints from which carpenters work in constructing buildings.

In some print shops the small volume of work does not warrant the employment of a layout man, so the compositors or foremen have to design and arrange the printing. It is necessary, therefore, for every compositor to have some knowledge of layout, and the ability to design printing.

There are two types of layout men, the TYPE LAYOUT MAN and the ART LAYOUT MAN. The type layout man is not necessarily an artist. He must, however, know type and the various printing methods, as this knowledge is necessary in designing layouts. He does not need to be able to draw, but he should be able to letter neatly. Any art work such as illustrations and borders will be traced by the type layout man rather than designed. The art layout man is a person who is an artist and specializes in layout. He is able to draw his illustrations as well as letter but usually does not have the necessary knowledge of the mechanics of printing which the type layout man must have.

Most type layout men are printers who have studied and advanced themselves. The purpose of the instruction in layout work is to give the printer the training which will help him to qualify as a type layout man.

Before one can begin the designing of printing, he should have a knowledge of type and the point system.

THE POINT SYSTEM

The printer uses a special system of measuring known as the point system. The point system is a method of measuring type that is based on a unit called a pica which is equal to approximately 1/6". For smaller measurements the pica is divided into 12 parts, each part being called a point.

1

The standard printers' measures are as follows:

Fig. 1

6 picas equals 1 inch
12 points equals 1 pica
72 points equals 1 inch (approx.)
6 points equals 1 nonpareil (half pica)
1 point equals about 1/72 inch

6 POINTS NONPAREIL   12 POINTS 1 PICA   6 PICAS 1 INCH

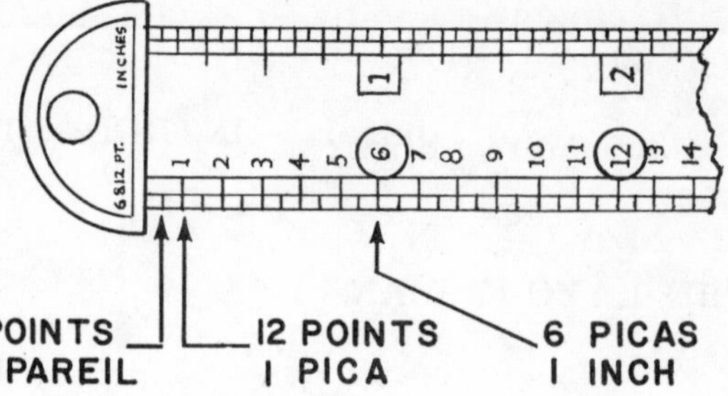

If the materials used by the compositor are cast according to the point system, they may be used interchangeably. The point system is an orderly method that enters into many calculations in printers' arithmetic and in the use of type and materials.

Before the point system came into general use, printers had different units of measurement. Each type founder (one who makes or casts type is called a type founder) had his own unit and this frequently differed slightly from that of every other type founder. The difference in size was so great that the same size type from two different founders could not be lined up in the same line without the use of thin strips of paper. Quads and spaces bought from one founder would not fit with type bought from another.

HISTORY OF THE POINT SYSTEM

Several attempts had been made by type founders before 1878 to improve upon the conditions mentioned, but no definite results had been obtained. About 1737 a French type founder named Pierre Simon Fournier had invented the point idea and had made it very nearly as perfect as we have it now.

Fournier's plan was not adopted by any American type founder until 1878 when the foundry of Marder, Luse and Co. of Chicago was destroyed by fire. When it was rebuilt the firm decided to cast all types and materials according to the point system. In 1887 the United States Type Founders Association adopted it, and today it is the only system in general use in print shops.

TYPE AND THE POINT SYSTEM

The point system is used to measure and designate type sizes. The size of type is its height or the depth of a line up and down the page. The width of the type is called its set.

Beginning with 6-point, the usual sizes are graduated by two points up to 14-point (6-, 8-, 12-, 14-) then 18-point. Larger sizes are then multiples of 6-point up to 60-point, (18-, 24-, 30-, 36-, 42-, 48-, 54-, 60-). Still larger sizes are 72-point, 84-point, 120-point and 144-point. The latter size is the largest type commonly cast in a mold.

Besides the sizes mentioned, there are several intermediate ones which are not frequently used, such as 7-point, 9-point, 11-point, etc. Sizes smaller than 6-point (4-, 4 1/2-, 5- and 5 1/2-point) are also made, but type smaller than 5-point is not practical for general use. These small sizes are employed for special purposes, like miniature editions of books, cut-in notes, foot-notes, etc. A 5 1/2-point measure, known as agate, is commonly used by newspapers and magazines. The agate line (14 lines to an inch) is considered the standard of measurement commonly used for advertizing space by newspapers and magazines.

When a line of 72-point type is printed the letters will not be 1 inch high when printed, as the face of the type sets back on the shoulder. The body of the type is 72 points or one inch and the face of the type will be less. Therefore, as the face of the type does not cover the entire body, it is difficult to know the exact body size of a letter by merely seeing it printed on paper.

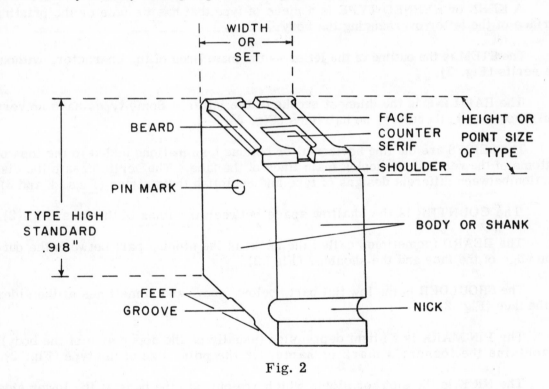

Fig. 2

PARTS OF TYPE

Every piece of type has various parts. The following is a description of each part.

On the BODY or SHANK, which is the largest part of the type, will be found the smaller members (Fig. 2).

The FACE consists of the stem, serifs and, on some types, the kern. The face is on top of the body and is the portion from which the printing is done when it comes in contact with the ink and paper (Fig. 2).

3

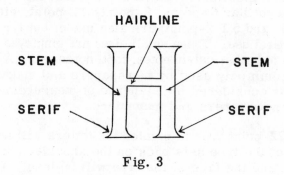

Fig. 3

A KERN or KERNED TYPE is a piece of type that has its face or the printing surface of the letter overhanging the body.

The STEM is the outline of the letter -- the main lines of the character, without the serifs (Fig. 3).

The HAIRLINE is the thinnest stroke of the letter. Some types have no very thin strokes and, therefore, no hairlines (Fig. 3).

The SERIFS are the fine horizontal or oblique terminations added to the tops or bottoms of the vertical or sloping main lines of the face. The serifs create the distinction between different designs of type and establish their styles (Figs. 2 and 3).

The COUNTER is the shallow space between the lines of the face (Fig. 2).

The BEARD (sometimes called the neck) is the sloping part between the outside edge of the face and the shoulder (Fig. 2).

The SHOULDER is the low flat part, below, above and sometimes at the sides of the face (Fig. 2).

The PIN MARK is a slight depression (usually on the upper side of the body). It contains the foundry's mark or name, or the point size of the type (Fig. 2).

The NICK is the slot, or slots, which are cut into the body at the lower side near the bottom of the type. There are nicks variously grouped on type, and they act as a guide for the compositor when he sets the type. After he sets a line, the nicks should all face outward, be of the same number and line up. By glancing at the nicks after the line is set, the compositor can quickly locate a letter than may belong to another font of type or one that may be upside down (Fig. 2).

The GROOVE is the hollow part at the bottom running across the width of the body, thereby forming the feet (Fig. 2).

The FEET are found at the bottom and are the two parts on each side of the groove which support the type (Fig. 2).

4

ASSIGNMENT

A. Complete the following sentences on a separate sheet. Do not write on this page.

1. It is important that the printer know how to make layouts because

_____

2. We designate the height or size of type by _____

3. The width of type is called its _____

4. Seventy-two point type when printed is not an inch high because

_____

5. There are _____ picas in one inch.

6. There are _____ points in one inch.

7. The point system was invented by _____

8. The point system has been in use in this country for about _____ years.

9. There are _____ points in one pica.

B. Identify the parts of the piece of type drawn below.

1. _____

2. _____

3. _____

4. _____

5. _____

6. _____

7. _____

8. _____

9. _____

10. _____

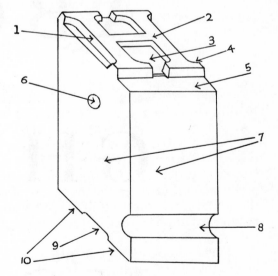

Unit 2   PRACTICE LETTERING (ROMAN)

ROMAN LETTERS

In order to design attractive layouts it is necessary to be able to letter neatly. Before studying the principles of layout, therefore, the student should practice the lettering of both Roman letters and Gothic letters as these are the two styles commonly used. Roman letters are composed of thick, or wide, and thin, or narrow, strokes. For example, notice how the letter A shown below is made with thick and thin strokes. Below are a few Roman letters which you will trace first and then letter freehand.

PROCEDURE

1. Place the first sheet in the layout pad over the letters below, making sure they are centered.

2. Trace the top row of letters, A to E, using a soft pencil with a sharp point.

3. In the space below the traced letters draw two light guide lines and copy the same letters freehand.

4. Repeat this procedure for rows G to M and N to S. Have the instructor check your lettering.

A B C D E

G H K L M

N O P R S

Unit 3   PRACTICE LETTERING (GOTHIC)

GOTHIC LETTERS

The letters printed below are known as Gothic letters. Any type face having the strokes all the same thickness or weight is called a Gothic type.

Gothic and Roman letters are not the only designs used for the printers' type. There are many other designs commonly used. More will be said about these other designs later but for your information samples of three are shown as follows:

SCRIPT   *Holiday*   CURSIVE   *Bristol*   TEXT   𝔅𝔲𝔣𝔣𝔞𝔩𝔬

PROCEDURE

1. Place a sheet from your layout pad over the letters below, making sure they are centered.

2. Trace the top row of letters, A to F, using a soft pencil with a sharp point.

3. In the space below the traced letters draw two light guide lines and copy the same letters freehand.

4. Repeat this procedure for rows G to M, and N to S. Have the instructor check your lettering.

A C D E F

G H K L M

N O P R S

Unit 4   SPACING AND FORMING WORDS

When you design a layout, you will have to place a word or a group of words in a certain amount of space. In order to do this, you should know how to form words and to space letters.

In spacing letters, try to keep the same amount of white space between the letters. In the word "Man" (Fig. 1) imagine that the letters are raised, and that we nail a board from the top of the M to the top of the A. Then we nail a board across the bottom between the two letters and pour cement between them. Now we wish to find where the letter N should be placed. We place the N far enough from the A so that we could board up the top and bottom between the two letters, and take the cement out of the space between M - A and pour it between A - N. If this is spaced correctly we will have just enough cement to fill the space. In other words, there will be the same amount of white space between the M and A as between the A and N. Area 1 = Area 2.

Fig. 1

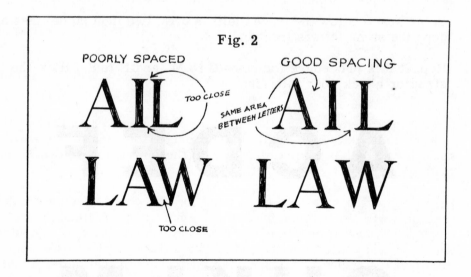

In designing printing it is usually necessary for the layout man to place words or lines of type to fit into a certain space. As there are a large variety of type sizes, it is up to the designer to select a size that he believes will fit the space. After trying it, he may find it too large. In that case a smaller size should be tested. In making this type selection the specimen sheets should always be used, and the spacing of the lettering should be similar to that on the specimen sheet so that it will cause the compositor no trouble when setting the line.

When lettering on layouts, do not try to imitate the type face you wish to use. Make a Roman type of letter with thick and thin strokes, or a Gothic letter with strokes the same thickness.

By changing the widths of the strokes, the letters can be made so that they will be about the tone or darkness desired. Instead of drawing the characteristics of each type design, the layout man marks the layout so that the compositor will know what style and size of type is wanted.

You will have no trouble making Gothic letters, as all of the strokes are the same width, but you will have to know which strokes are thick or which are thin when making the Roman letters. In type faces having thick and thin strokes all strokes slanting toward the left are thin except the letter Z. All strokes slanting the opposite way are thick. All vertical or up and down strokes are thick except the letters N, M and U. Both strokes on the N are thin. In the M the first stroke is thin and the second thick. In the U the first stroke is thick and second thin. All the thick strokes must be the same width. All the thin strokes must be the same width.

ASSIGNMENT

1. In the center of the next blank page in the layout pad draw a rectangular page measuring 28 picas wide and 42 picas deep.

2. Inside the rectangular page place a marginal line 3 picas from the edge of all four sides.

3. Inside these marginal lines the four words, BEAUTY, SPEED, POWER and STEEL will be lettered.

4. Secure specimens of type faces from your instructor and select type designs that you believe will be appropriate for each of the words to be lettered. Show your selections to the instructor so that he may guide you.

5. Decide upon the size type to be used for the word, "Beauty," making certain it will set between the two marginal lines. A standard method employed by layout men is to use the specimen type sheets, measuring the set or width of each letter and testing it on the layout to see whether it will fit the space. This accurate measuring of each letter assures the layout man that the type will actually fit the space in the selected size when the compositor sets it.

6. After the guide lines, indicating the size of the type and the spacing of the letters, have been lightly drawn, faintly sketch in the shape of each letter.

7. With a soft, sharp-pointed pencil letter the word so that it resembles the type you have selected. Mark the name of the type and its size opposite the word but outside the 28 pica by 42 pica page.

8. Follow the same procedure for each of the other words.

Unit 5   PROPORTION AND PLACING ONE UNIT ON A PAGE

PROPORTION

It is necessary at times for the printer or designer of printing to select the size sheet for a job. Therefore, he should know pleasing proportions in order to be able to choose well proportioned sheets. Note poor proportions in Fig. 1.

One good proportion to use is the "two by three" or "Regular Oblong." A sheet using this proportion will be two parts wide and three parts deep (Fig. 2).

If a customer wants a menu cover to be 4 inches wide and a height that will be in proportion, find the measurement by using the Regular Oblong. As the width is 4 inches, it should be divided into two parts, giving 2 inches in each part. This 2-inch part should then be placed up the side three times (or multiplied by three) and this would give the height of 6 inches. Therefore, the menu cover 4 inches wide by 6 inches deep will be well proportioned. Knowing one measure, the other can always be found in the above manner.

Fig. 1	Fig. 2
POORLY PROPORTIONED PAGES	WELL PROPORTIONED PAGE

A square page is uninteresting as each side is the same measure.

A tall slender page is poorly proportioned as its depth is too great for its width.

REGULAR OBLONG

Divide width into two parts. Take measurement of one part and place up the side three times for depth.

If a printer has only one word to place on a page, he should not locate it in the exact vertical center as is commonly believed. If it were placed in the center (Fig. 3), the page would be divided into two uninteresting, evenly divided parts. The best location is above the center on the "The Line of Golden Proportion."

In order to find the location for a single word, divide the page from the top to the bottom into eight even divisions. The third division from the top is called "The Line of Golden Proportion" and is used by layout men and printers as the ideal location for one word or a group of words. Place the word on this line so that half of each letter extends above this line and the other half of each letter below the line. In this way three-eighths of the space will be left above the word and five-eighths below.

INCORRECT METHODS OF PLACING ONE WORD ON A PAGE

Fig. 3   Fig. 4   Fig. 5   Fig. 6

MENU   MENU   MENU   MENU

POOR- One word shouldn't be centered on the page.

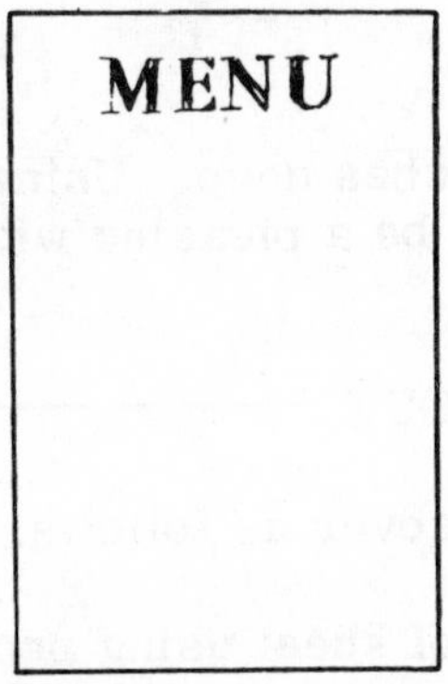

POOR- Too high. It looks as if it were being pushed off the page.

POOR- Too large for easy reading at arm's length. Good for a poster.

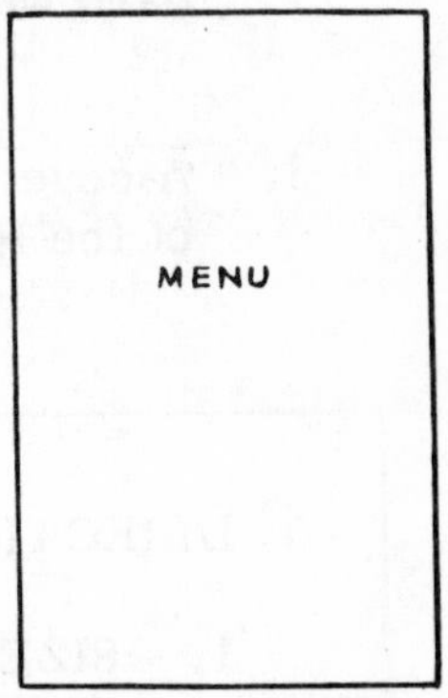

POOR- Too small for the sheet size. Would be lost on the page.

Fig. 7

CORRECT METHOD

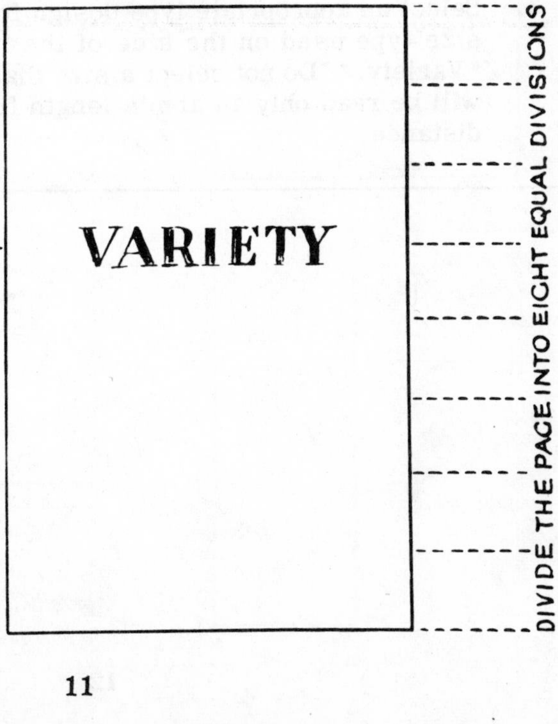

LINE OF GOLDEN PROPORTION

One word should be placed half above this line and half below.

VARIETY

DIVIDE THE PACE INTO EIGHT EQUAL DIVISIONS

11

PROBLEMS

Figure the following and show the instructor your answers and the figures used in getting the answers.

1. A customer wishes to place an advertisement in a program and wants it to be 24 picas wide. Using the proportion of the Regular Oblong, what would be a pleasing depth for the advertisement?

2. A counter card is to be designed and any one of the following sizes may be used:, 8 in. by 12 in., 6 in. by 12 in., 4 1/2 in. by 12 in. Which of the three would be the best to select if a well proportioned card were desired?

3. A cover for a booklet must be 3 inches deep. Using the proportion of the Regular Oblong, what would be a pleasing width?

THE LAYOUT

DIRECTIONS: Make a layout for a cover as follows:

1. SIZE: 6 in. wide. Find depth of sheet using proportion of the Regular Oblong.

2. Place the word VARIETY on the page.

3. Select an appropriate type design for the word and mark the size type used on the side of the layout opposite the word "Variety." Do not select a size that is too large. The word will be read only an arm's length from a person, not a long distance.

Unit 6   PROPORTION AND ONE GROUP ON A PAGE

GOLDEN OBLONG

Besides the Regular Oblong which has been explained, there are three other proportions commonly used by printers. They are the Golden Oblong, Printers Oblong and the Hypotenuse Oblong. Of the three the Golden Oblong is the most popular. This oblong, believed by the early Greek architects and designers to be the most beautiful proportion, is used today by most designers of printing to secure a pleasing page relationship. The width of the oblong is three-fifths the depth, or three parts wide and five parts deep. Using the width of a page to find a well proportioned depth, divide the width into three parts and take the measurement of one part; place it up the side five times and the result will be the depth of the page.

ONE GROUP ON A PAGE

When designing printing, it is necessary at times to place only one group of words on a page. As in finding the location for one word, the line of Golden Proportion (3/8 down the page) is used to locate the main display or display group. If the group is centered on the line of Golden Proportion with half the group above the line and half below, it should have a pleasing arrangement.

When arranging a small group, it is best to use only one family of type. If two or three different type designs were used in one group, they would tend to make the characteristics of the type distract attention from the message.

PROBLEMS

Figure the following and show the instructor your figures and answers.

1. An owner of a restaurant wants a menu printed and desires to have it 7 1/2 in. deep. Using the proportion of the Golden Oblong, what would be a pleasing width to suggest for this menu?

2. A customer wants a well proportioned booklet and gives the printer the following three sizes to choose from: 6 in. by 10 in., 6 in. by 15 in., 6 in. by 7 1/2 in. Using the proportion of the Golden Oblong, which would be the best size to select for the booklet?

THE LAYOUT

COVER COPY

SIZE: 5 1/2 in. wide. (Using Golden Oblong proportion, find the depth)

COPY: The New Hudson Six and Eight

DIRECTIONS

1. Find the line of Golden proportion as explained in Unit 5 and place half the group above this line and half below.

2. As the word "Hudson" is important, select an appropriate size for easy reading.

3. Do not have the size of type in the other lines too large or too small but about half the size of the word "Hudson."

4. Remember that an "en" quad will be placed between the words when set, so leave that amount of space in the layout.

5. Select an appropriate type design and show the instructor your selection.

6. After making a proper selection of type and type size, draw the finished layout.

7. Mark the type size and the name of the type opposite each line outside of the page.

POOR- The word Hudson should be accented a little more than the other words. →

THE NEW
HUDSON
SIX AND EIGHT

THE NEW
HUDSON
SIX AND EIGHT

POOR- Too great a contrast in type sizes. The word "Hudson" should be only about twice the size of the other words. ←

POOR- Grouping of type is poor. Type forms a shape which points in the direction opposite the natural direction of reading →

THE NEW
HUDSON
SIX AND EIGHT

THE NEW
HUDSON
SIX AND EIGHT

GOOD- Note the pleasing relationship of the type sizes and the shape of the group. ←

Unit 7   SHAPE HARMONY

SHAPE OF TYPE PAGE AND PAPER PAGE

When type is placed on a sheet of paper, it should harmonize with the sheet. That is, the shape of the type page or group should harmonize with the shape of the paper. A wide group of type on a narrow page is not pleasing, as there is no relationship between the type and the page. The long side of the type group should be parallel to the long side of the page, and the short side parallel to the short side of the page. Fig. 1 shows an example of poor shape harmony; the shape of the type group is too wide for the shape of the page and does not look balanced. In Fig. 2 the shape has been changed so that it harmonizes with the shape of the page. Therefore, it gives a pleasing appearance.

The shape of the type should also harmonize with the shape of the page or group. Condensed type looks best on a narrow page or column (Fig. 2) whereas extended type requires a wider page (Fig. 3). Type of ordinary width is most desirable for the general run of work, since it can be used on pages of regular proportion or even on those of irregular shape if they are not too exaggerated.

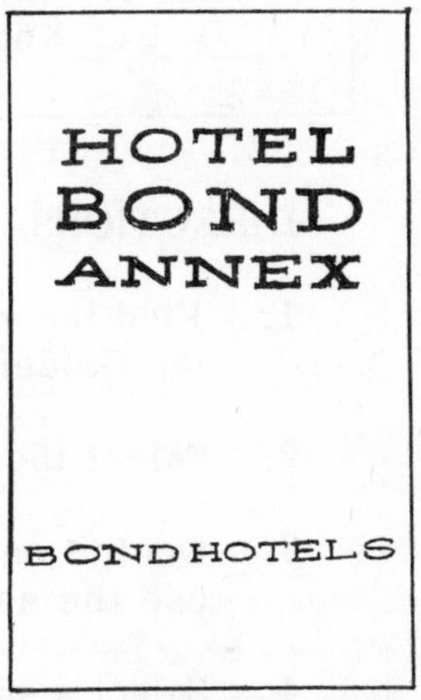

In general, it may be said that the shape of the page should dictate the shape of the type page and the type face selected.

PLACING TWO GROUPS OF TYPE

As previously explained, a single word or group of type should be placed 3/8 down the page on the line of Golden Proportion. If an additional line or group is placed at the bottom of the page, this will change the location of the main display group.

HOTEL
BOND
ANNEX

BOND HOTELS

Fig. 1 *POOR — Type groups are not the same shape as the shape of the page*

Fig. 3
Type group is the same shape as page shape and type is wide or extended

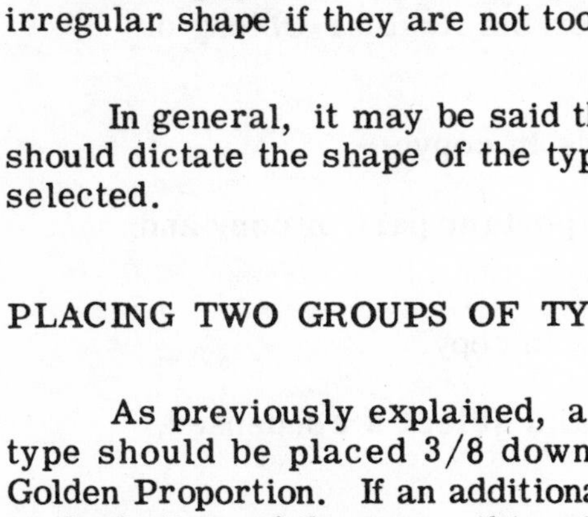

HOTEL BOND
ANNEX

BOND HOTELS

Fig. 2 ⟶
Good Shape Harmony. Type is set into a shape that is similar to the shape of the page. The use of a condensed type also harmonizes with the style of the page.

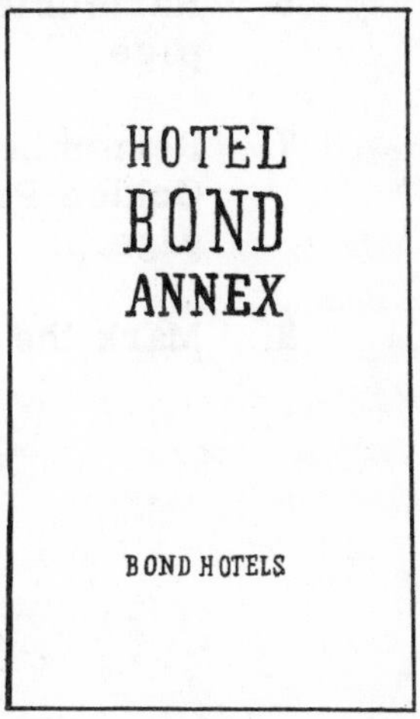

HOTEL
BOND
ANNEX

BOND HOTELS

15

PRINTING LAYOUT AND DESIGN

Instead of being centered on the line of Golden Proportion, the copy will be moved upward so as to maintain a variety of space and a pleasing balance. There is no standard method for finding the correct location but the layout man must use his judgment.

THE LAYOUT

COVER COPY

SIZE: The customer desires to have the cover 6 in. deep. You are to suggest a pleasing width.

COPY: The New Knox for Men
Knox Hat Co.

DIRECTIONS

1. Find the width of the page by using either the Regular Oblong or the Golden Oblong.

2. Select the most important word or words in copy.

3. Decide on size and style of type for important part of copy and use the same type design throughout.

4. Select a suitable size type for other words in copy.

5. Consider the shape of the paper page and select a condensed, regular or extended type to harmonize.

6. Harmonize the shape of your type groups with the shape of the page.

7. Remember that the large group will be placed above the Line of Golden Proportion because of the small group at the foot of the page.

8. Mark the layout so that the compositor can set it.

Unit 8   ARRANGEMENT OF SEVERAL UNITS

Instruction has been given in the placing of one and two groups of type on a page, so now it is necessary to consider the arrangement of several groups or units.

The printing of advertising pieces quite often involves the spending of hundreds of dollars by the advertiser. The cost of producing a small folder may be several hundred dollars, and advertisements that are placed in magazines cost thousands of dollars. For the space in just one national weekly magazine the advertiser must pay between $5000 and $20,000 for a full page advertisement. This does not include the layout, art work, typesetting and plate making. Therefore, because of this expense, considerable thought should be given the arrangement of the layout so that it will bring results.

The copy of a printed piece might contain a cut or picture (Fig. 1), a display head (Fig. 2), text or reading matter (Fig. 3) and a signature and location (Fig. 4). These are the four separate units with which the layout man works. With these four units he must create an arrangement that will bring the advertiser results.

Fig. 1   Fig. 3

SPRING HATS   DORN HAT SHOP, NEW YORK
Fig. 2   Fig. 4

It is necessary to have a method or system of arranging the printing. First in order to have the advertisement read, it is necessary to attract the reader's attention. Therefore, the copy should be studied and one unit selected that will serve this purpose. Usually the cut is used, for most persons are interested in pictures and will look at them. If the cut is selected as the unit to be used to attract attention, it should be placed near the top of the page, as it is natural for a person to read from top to bottom.

After the reader's attention has been gained, it will be necessary to hold his interest. Therefore, from the copy something should be selected that will create this interest. The display head, as it is called, usually fulfills this purpose. If the copy contains several display lines, it is necessary for the layout man to select the line that will create the most interest. The eye is naturally attracted to a picture, so the display head selected should be placed near the cut where the reader will be sure to see it.

After the reader has become interested he will want to know more about the product, so that body matter or text should be placed next. This text or reading matter should tend to create a desire. If the reader desires to purchase the product, he will want to know where to secure it. The name of the company (called the signature) should be placed after the body to give this information.

Therefore a piece of printing should be designed to accomplish the following:

1. Attract attention - a picture or cut
2. Create interest - the display head
3. Create a desire - the text or body
4. Tell how to satisfy the desire - the signature and location

When designing printing that contains several units, small sketches should be made before deciding upon the finished layout. These small sketches are called "thumbnail" sketches. (Fig. 5) Sometimes as many as 20 of these sketches are made before the layout man is satisfied that he has sketched the most effective layouts.

As an example, a job to be designed may contain the following units:

1. A cut of a hat

2. A display head SPRING HATS

3. Text or reading matter

4. Signature and location DORN HAT SHOP. NEW YORK

The first step in designing the advertisement is to make the thumbnail sketches as suggested below. Notice in Fig. 5 how the positions of the units have been altered.

Fig. 5

After the thumbnails have been made they should be studied and the best one selected. The finished layout should then be made to present to the customer. After the customer accepts it, the compositor may work from this same finished layout or from a tracing of it.

When making the finished layout, all large display type should be lettered in the size of type to be used. The text may be indicated by lines ruled as shown in Fig. 6. The cuts will be traced from photographs supplied by the instructor or, in actual practice, photographs supplied by the customer.

When you come to the New York
World's Fair, be sure to visit our
display room at 100 Sixth Avenue.

Fig. 6

THE LAYOUT

Arrange the following publication advertisement:

SIZE: 24 picas by 40 picas deep

DISPLAY HEAD: Tower Rooms

CUT: 8 picas by 14 picas deep

TEXT: Use as much room for the text as desired. Copy would be written after the layout is completed. The usual procedure is to make the layout and then write the text to fill the space although in many instances the copy is given to the designer and he has to figure the amount of space it is to occupy.

SIGNATURE: Copley Plaza
Central Park South

DIRECTIONS

1. Make four thumbnail sketches, keeping the proportions of the cut and other units the same as in the copy. Have the instructor check them.

2. After one design is selected, make the finished layout.

3. When making the finished layout, leave a 3 pica margin around the entire layout inside the 24 by 40 pica measurements.

4. Select an appropriate type design, using only one family of type for both the display head and the signature.

5. Mark the name of the type and size opposite each line for the compositor.

Unit 9   METHOD OF CUTTING PAPER

When planning and designing printing, it is often necessary to be able to figure the cutting of paper. Paper, when purchased, is in large sheets and if the job is to be printed on a small sheet, it is necessary to know the method of finding the number of small sheets that can be cut from a large one with a minimum of waste.

Suppose an advertisement to be designed is 6″ × 9″ deep, and the large sheet from which the paper is to be cut measures 25″ × 38″. The layout man wants to know if this size stock for the advertisement can be cut from the large sheet without a great deal of waste.

The method for figuring how to cut small sheets from large sheets is as follows:

1. Mark down the dimensions of the large sheet.

2. Below the large sheet dimensions mark down the dimensions of the small sheet.

3. Divide diagonally ⎰ Find the number of times
4. Divide vertically ⎱ the small number will go evenly into the large number.

Example:

┌─────────────────────┐
│ Dividing Diagonally │
└─────────────────────┘

$$2 \times 6$$

Sheet to be cut 25 × 38   25 × 38 = twelve 6 × 9 sheets can be cut from
Size desired   6 × 9   6 × 9   a 25 × 38 sheet by this method.

$$1 \quad 1$$

┌─────────────────────┐
│ Dividing Vertically │
└─────────────────────┘

$$4 \quad 4$$

Sheet to be cut 25 × 38   25 × 38   Sixteen 6 × 9 sheets can be cut from
Size desired   6 × 9   6 × 9   = a 25 × 38 sheet by this method.

$$1 \quad 1$$

Thus, it would be more economical to cut the short dimension of the piece of 6″ × 9″ out of the short dimension of the 25″ × 38″. On the short 25″ side there will be four 9″ cuts. This will give sixteen 6″ × 9″ pieces out of the large sheet as shown in Fig. 1.

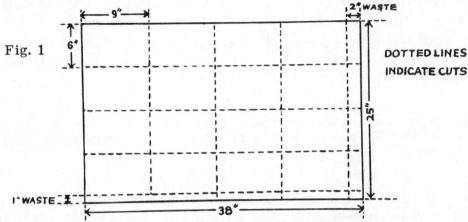

Fig. 1

DOTTED LINES
INDICATE CUTS

At times this above method will not give the greatest number obtainable from a sheet. For example, there may be some scrap sheets 7″ × 13″ from which are to be cut 3″ × 4″ pieces. Figuring in the usual manner 6 would be the number that might be cut from one sheet.

Vertically

$$\begin{matrix} 3 & 2 \\ \frac{13 \times 7}{4 \times 3} & = 3 \times 2 = 6 \text{ out} \\ 1 & 1 \end{matrix}$$

Diagonally

$$\begin{matrix} 4 & 1 \\ \frac{13 \times 7}{4 \times 3} & = 4 \times 1 = 4 \text{ out} \\ 1 & 1 \end{matrix}$$

When dividing diagonally, the 4″ will divide into the 7″ side only once leaving 3″ waste. Therefore, it might be possible to use that 3″ waste and cut more than 6 out. After diagraming it as in Fig. 2, it is found that 7 may be cut from the one sheet.

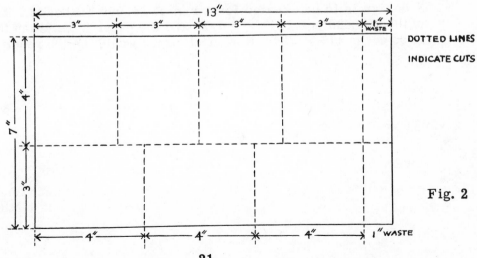

DOTTED LINES
INDICATE CUTS

Fig. 2

21

ASSIGNMENT PROBLEMS

Figure the following problems and have the instructor correct them after you have completed the work.

1. A job is to be designed which will be on a sheet 3 1/2″ × 6 1/4″ and is to be cut from a sheet 28″ × 44″. How many pieces would be cut from one large 28″ × 44″ sheet?

2. A job has been designed that is 4 1/2″ × 6″ and may be cut from either a 25″ × 38″ sheet or a 28″ × 44″ sheet. Which large sheet would it be better to use? Show your work.

3. A small mailing card 3″ × 5″ is to be designed and scrap paper 8″ × 16″ is to be used. There are 100 of these scrap 8″ × 16″ sheets. How many mailing cards can be printed? Make a small diagram showing how the paper will be cut.

4. An advertisement that the customer wants to measure 4″ in width is to be designed. By using the proportions of the Regular Oblong, find the depth. After securing the measurements of this advertisement, find the number of pieces that may be cut from one sheet of 25″ × 38″ stock.

5. A piece of printing to be designed may be either 4″ × 6″ or 5″ × 5″. If the stock to be used on the job were to be 28″ × 42″, which would be the better size to use in designing the job so as to get the least waste when cutting the stock?

6. A design is to be created for a run of 16,000 billheads. The size of the billhead is 8 1/2″ × 5 1/2″ and the paper from which they are to be cut is 17″ × 22″. How much paper would the job require?

Unit 10   TYPES OF BALANCE

Before starting the thumbnail sketches for a layout, the copy should always be studied and a decision made as to the type of balance that would be most appropriate.

There are two types of balance. One is called the FORMAL or Bi-symmetrical balance (Fig. 1) and the other the INFORMAL or Occult balance (Fig. 2). When all of the units are centered, that is, arranged so that half are on one side and half on the other side of an imaginary line drawn through the middle of the layout, that is a formal balance (Fig. 1). If the units are arranged off center, it is an informal balance (Fig. 2).

Fig. 1

Fig. 2

FORMAL BALANCE

INFORMAL BALANCE

The formal type of balance would probably be employed when the advertisement is for a bank, insurance company, or any company that wishes to give the impression of being very stable and secure. When designing advertising for expensive or exclusive products such as jewelry or high class automobiles, the formal type of balance should be used to help give the desired impression. As formal balance gives the impression of being orderly, quiet and dignified, it will not be appropriate for all jobs.

If the copy appears to require an arrangement that is full of pep, it will need to be dynamically arranged. In this case the informal type of balance will be very appropriate.

Therefore, before starting thumbnail sketches, decide whether the advertisement should be formal or informal.

THE LAYOUT

SIZE: 6″ × 9″ deep

DISPLAY HEAD: Years of Experience

CUT: 14 picas by 11 picas deep

TEXT: The copy would be written after the layout has been completed. Therefore, no definite amount of space is to be
saved for the text.

SIGNATURE: The Travelers
Hartford, Connecticut

DIRECTIONS

1. Make two thumbnail sketches after you decide the type of balance you
believe should be employed.

2. Select the thumbnail sketch you believe to be the better and have the
instructor check it.

3. Select a type you believe to be appropriate and make the finished layout.

4. Mark the layout completely.

Unit 11   METHOD OF BALANCING UNITS

The first principle of type layout which should be mastered is balance. In the previous unit formal and informal balance were explained but there are many principles which now must be learned about balancing the various units of a layout.

The two outstanding units of the design should first be selected. The outstanding units might be two type groups, or two cuts or some other parts. The next step is to balance the two units selected about a line called the optical center. Because of an optical illusion, the real or mathematical center will strike the eye as being too low (Fig. 1). For this reason, a line slightly above the true center is used as the axis about which the two outstanding units of the design are to be balanced (Fig. 2). This line, known as the optical center, is approximately 1/10 the distance from the true center to the top of the page above the true center. The layout man, however, does not actually measure this distance.

The principles of balance are very simple but in some layouts very difficult to apply. If one imagines the optical center as the point of balance of a seesaw, it simplifies the positioning of units on a page so that they balance. If two boys weighing the same sit the same distance from the point of balance of a seesaw, they will balance.

Therefore, two cuts or two groups of type that are about the same size should be placed about the same distance from the optical center (Fig. 3).

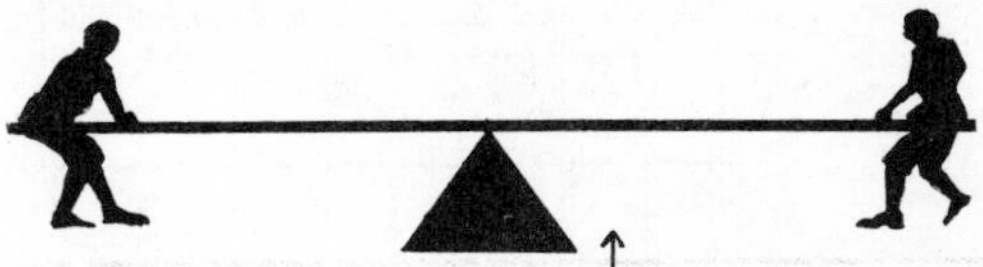

Fig. 1

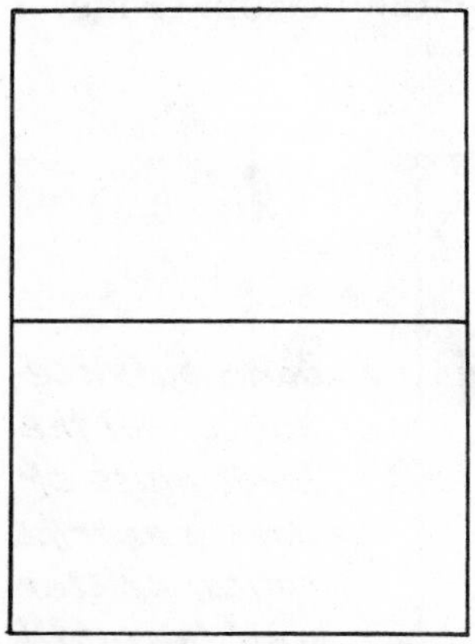

Fig. 2

Fig. 3

This page is divided into two equal parts with the line in the measured center—but it appears to the eye to be below center.

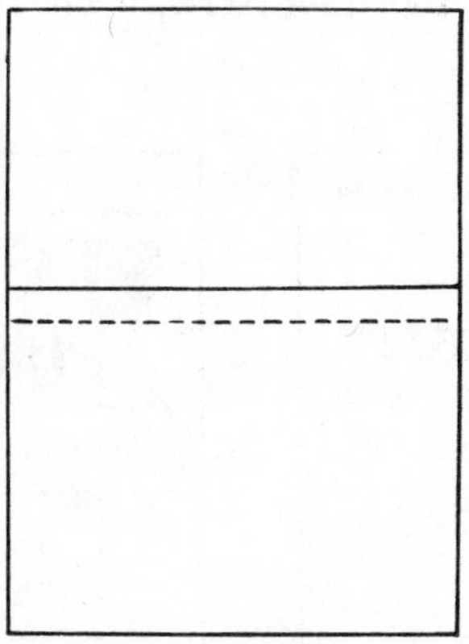

This line is above the center but to the eye it appears to be in the center of the page. This is known as the Optical Center.

Just as two boys the same size should be the same distance from the center of a see-saw in order to balance—two cuts the same size should be the same distance from the optical center.

If a large boy tried to balance with a small boy, he would have to move nearer to the center (Figs. 4 and 5).

Fig. 4   Fig. 5

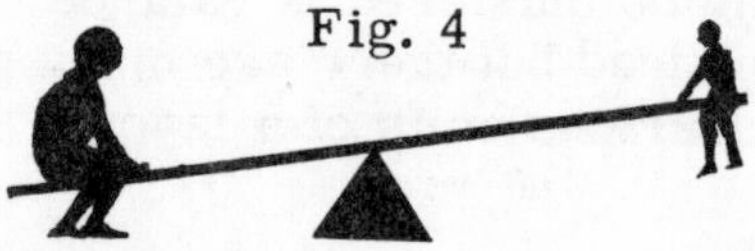

The large boy sitting the same distance from the center as the small one will force the small boy to go up...if they wish to balance, the large boy should sit near the center.

Fig. 6

OPTICAL

CENTER

BETTER than we thought!

TASTY BREADS

Likewise, if we have groups of type or cuts of unequal size, the larger unit should be placed nearer the optical center than the smaller one (Fig. 6).

The large boy must sit nearer the center of the seesaw in order to balance. — Therefore the larger cut must be placed nearer the center. After the cuts are balanced, other units are easily placed.

The balance of "darks" should also be considered. A heavy black at the top of the page should be balanced by something dark, a cut or type, near the bottom (Figs. 7 and 8).

Fig. 7

Poor balance of darks. Dark above the optical center should be balanced by a dark unit below the optical center.

STEEL
for Industry

S and A STEEL

STEEL
for Industry

S and A STEEL

Fig. 8

Darks balance. Notice that the large mass of dark is near the optical center and the small mass further away

Color should also be balanced. A color at the top of a page should be balanced by a small amount of color near the bottom.

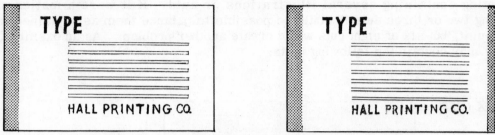

Fig. 9   *When color is used near the top of a page, it should be balanced by color at the bottom. When color is on one side of a page, it should be repeated on the other side.*   Fig. 10

Before making thumbnail sketches for a job, the two outstanding units should be selected and balanced. After these units are balanced, the other parts of the design will be easily placed (Fig. 6).

THE LAYOUT

SIZE: 8 1/2 in. by 11 in. deep

CUT: 3 1/2 in. by 4 in. deep

DISPLAY HEAD: Start drinking Sanka Coffee

TEXT: Use as much space as desired for the text matter. The copy would be written after the layout is completed.

SMALL CUT: 4 in. by 1 1/2 in. deep

SIGNATURE: Sanka Coffee

DIRECTIONS

1. Decide upon the type of balance that should be employed in arranging the advertisement and make three thumbnail sketches, making sure that the cuts balance.

2. After having the thumbnail sketches checked by the instructor, make the finished layout.

3. Mark the layout for the compositor.

Unit 12   ARRANGING COPY CONTAINING MORE THAN TWO CUTS

Every printer at one time or other is confronted with the problem of arranging printing containing several illustrations or cuts. If it were a matter of arranging two or three cuts it would be possible to balance them as explained in the last unit, but six or eight cuts would create another problem. As an example, the copy may contain the following units:

SIX CUTS

DISPLAY HEAD   *NEW!*

TEXT

SIGNATURE   PEP-O GASOLINE

28

If the layout were arranged as in the thumbnail sketch (Fig. 1) it would appear very disorganized and spotty. Therefore, it is necessary for the designer to have a system of arranging the numerous units.

A tested and proven method is that of forming the layout after one of the following letters: C, U, T, Y, O, S. The letter employed will be regulated by the units in the copy. For example, the "PEP-O" advertisement may be arranged successfully using the U formation (Fig. 2) when it might not be possible to arrange it in any of the other formations.

Fig. 1 ⟶

Poorly arranged — The cuts give the layout a separated spotty appearance. The eye would have to jump around too much in order to read the advertisement.

The letter "U" would appear in this form. The letter would not be drawn but cuts and display type would form the shape of the "U" ⟵ Fig. 2 ⟶ *Compare this sketch with Fig. 1. Note how much easier it would be to read. The eye would travel easily from cut to cut.*

Below are a few sketches employing other letters (Fig. 3).

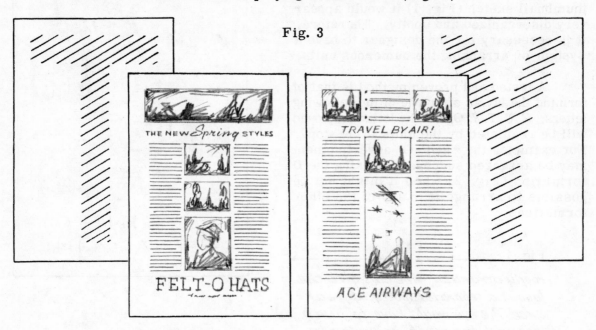

Fig. 3

The letter S is considered by designers to be the most pleasing arrangement as it swings the reader's eye down the page, giving the layout a swinging movement or rhythm (Fig. 4).

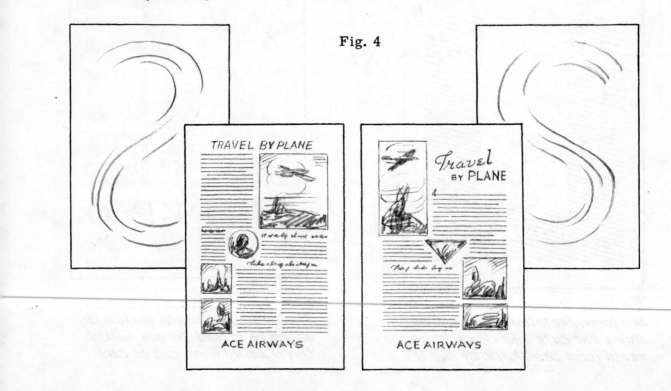

Fig. 4

┌─────────────────────────── THE LAYOUT ───────────────────────────┐

Select either the copy under (A) or (B) and make a finished layout following the directions listed below.

COPY (A)

SIZE: 8 1/2″ by 11″ deep

DISPLAY HEAD: America's Finest Car

TEXT: The copy would be written after the layout has been completed. Therefore, no definite amount of space is to be saved for the text.

LARGE CUT: 3 1/2″ by 5″ deep

CIRCULAR CUT: 1 1/2″ in diameter

SMALL CUTS: (Two) each 1″ by 1 1/2″ deep

SIGNATURE: Chrysler

COPY (B)

SIZE: 8 1/2″ by 11″ deep

DISPLAY HEAD: It Has Everything

TEXT: The copy would be written after the layout has been completed. Therefore, no definite amount of space is to be saved for the text.

LARGE CUT: 3 1/2″ by 4″ deep

CUT: Triangular shaped cut, each side 2 1/2″

SMALL CUT: 1 1/2″ by 2 1/2″ deep

SIGNATURE: Plymouth, now only $1865

└──┘

DIRECTIONS

1. Make four thumbnail sketches and submit them to the instructor for approval.

2. After one of the thumbnail sketches has been selected and approved, make the finished layout.

3. In layout work it is good practice to arrange an illustration so that it forces the reader's eyes to travel toward the center or an important part of the advertisement. If the illustration shows a living object, arrange the cut so that it is looking or heading into the layout. If the illustration shows a moving object, arrange the cut so that the line of motion is into or in the direction the layout man wishes the eye to travel. Trace the cuts so that the illustration faces into the layout or in the direction you wish the eye to move.

4. Mark the layout for the compositor in blue pencil.

REVIEW TEST

Write the answers to the following questions:

1. How many inches high is a piece of type from its feet to its face?

2. What part of a piece of type is the beard?

3. Where, on a sheet of paper, should one word be placed?

4. If a customer wishes to have a job printed on a sheet 4 inches wide, what would be a well proportioned depth to suggest to him? (Use either the proportion of the Regular Oblong or the Golden Oblong).

5. Make two thumbnail sketches showing the difference between good shape harmony and poor shape harmony.

6. What are the two types of balance?

7. Explain how a small cut and a large one should be spaced on a page so as to achieve balance.

8. How many points are there in an agate?

9. How many pieces of 8 1/2" by 11" stock can be cut from 100 sheets of 22" by 34" paper?

10. List at least six letters after which a layout containing several cuts may be arranged.

11. If a page of type measures 4 1/4" in width and 6 1/8" in depth, what would be the dimensions in points?

12. What is the optical center and where on a page is it located?

13. What is a kerned piece of type?

14. About how long has the point system of measure been used by the printers and type founders in America?

15. Where is the counter located on a piece of type?

16. What is the difference between a script type and a cursive type?

17. About how long was the point system of measure used in Europe before it was adopted by the type founders of this country?

18. What is the difference between a Roman type and a Gothic type?

Unit 13   SINGLE PAGE MARGINS

The layout man, or designer of printing, should always give careful consideration to the white space, or margins, around a printed page. The amount of marginal space is regulated by the arrangement of the page. A page containing considerable copy would have to be set in a small size type and the margins should be narrow. If the marginal space were wide, it would make the type appear crowded, as though the designer had jammed the type together in order to have wide margins. A page set in large sizes of type and arranged with considerable white space would require wide margins. If a printed page that is very open had narrow margins, the reader would undoubtedly feel that the job should have been printed on a larger size sheet. When all parts of a page are very open and the type large in size, the marginal space should also be wide. Therefore, a page that appears crowded should have narrow margins and an open page should have wide margins.

The white margin space around a page should not be the same on each side (Fig. 1), but should vary. It has been found that the most pleasing arrangement for single page margins is to have the two sides the same and narrowest, top a little wider, and the foot or bottom widest (Fig. 2).

Fig. 1   Fig. 2

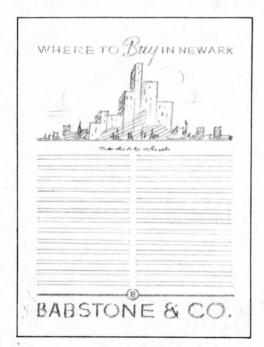

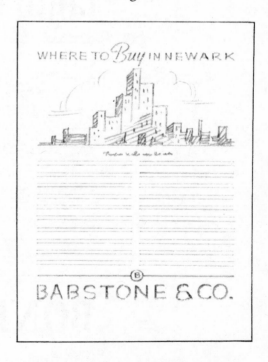

The margin at the foot of the page being narrow gives the entire layout the impression of being crowded at the bottom.

A pleasing arrangement of the margins with the widest margin at the foot of the page.

The bottom margin on all printed matter should be widest because the human eye believes the center of the page (optional center) to be above the actual measured center. Therefore, if we balance the type page on the optical center line, as discussed in a previous unit, the bottom margin will be wider than the top and the type will appear centered to the reader.

THE LAYOUT

DIRECTIONS

1. On the layout pad mark a page 4 in. by 6 in. deep.

2. Trace the layout for "Bond Press," placing it in its 4 in. by 6 in. space so as to have pleasing margins.

GOOD PRINTING

BOND PRESS

Unit 14   BOOK PAGE MARGINS

When a sheet of paper is folded, the crease divides it into two facing pages, as in books, and a new condition arises with respect to the placing of type groups on the pages and the treatment of margins. If we follow the method for laying out margins described in the previous unit and assume that each page is a separate sheet, the two pages will appear as in Fig. 1. In this case the two margins joined together at the fold form a wide band of white larger than any of the remaining margins, which separates the two type pages so that they seem to have nothing in common. For this reason we cannot use the method described in Unit 13.

Fig. 1

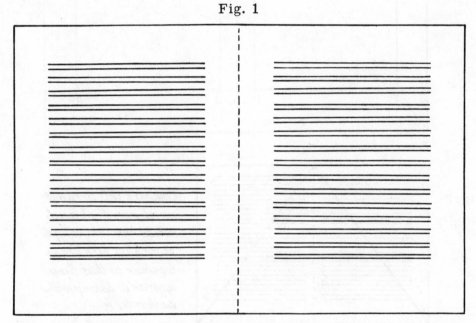

The wide marginal space at the fold or gutter appears to separate the two type pages — therefore this is not a satisfactory method of handling margins

The margins in Fig. 1 could be made more pleasing if the two type pages were brought closer together. There is no set rule which tells how close together to bring the type pages or how to proportion the margins, but there are several approved methods of establishing the marginal space.

In all pleasing arrangements of book margins, it will be found that there is a regular progression of widths beginning with the inner margin as the narrowest, the head or top being slightly wider, the outside margins next in width and the bottom or foot widest.

Of the several approved methods of arranging margins in a book, the following two seem to be the most popular.

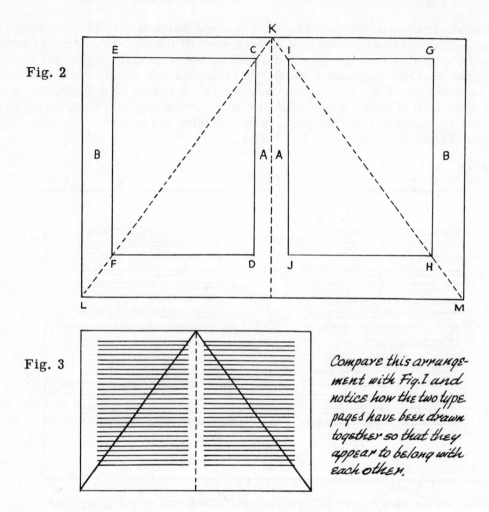

Fig. 2

Fig. 3

Compare this arrangement with Fig. 1 and notice how the two type pages have been drawn together so that they appear to belong with each other.

METHOD USED IN FIG. 2

1. After considering the size type to be used, select an appropriate width for the outside margin (B).
2. Have the margin at the gutter (A) one half that on the outside (B) and draw vertical lines CD, EF, GH and IJ.
3. Draw the diagonal lines KL and KM.
4. Where the diagonal lines cross the vertical lines at C and I the top margin will be located. Draw the top marginal lines CE and IG.
5. Where the diagonal crosses at F and H will be located the bottom margin, so draw the marginal lines FD and JH.
6. The margins will, therefore, appear as in Fig. 3 with the inside narrowest, top a little wider, outside still wider and bottom widest.

Fig. 4

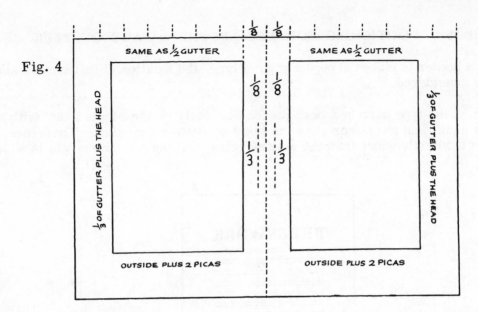

METHOD EMPLOYED IN FIG. 4

1. Divide the width of each page into eight parts. One of these parts will give the measurement of the inner margin (gutter) which is therefore one eighth of the page width.

2. The head should be the same width as the inner margin.

3. Take one third of the two inner margins (the complete gutter) and add that to the measurement of the head in order to find the width of the outside margin.

4. The margin at the bottom or foot of the page should be equal to the measurement of the outside margin plus two picas.

THE LAYOUT

DIRECTIONS

1. Draw two book pages in the layout pad. Each page will measure 8 in. by 6 in. deep (Fig. 5) with the fold in the center.

2. Draw a dotted line to indicate the fold.

3. Find the proper margins, using the diagonal method. The type will be set 18 picas wide.

4. On the other set of book pages that have been drawn show another method of finding book page margins.

Unit 15   POSITIONING BORDERS AROUND A PAGE OF TYPE

When a border is placed around a page of type, the location of that border should be carefully considered.

In Fig. 1 the type page has been placed correctly on the single sheet with each side margin equal and narrower than the head or bottom margins. Therefore, the head margin is slightly wider than the side margins, and the bottom margin is widest.

Fig. 1

In Fig. 2 the type is located correctly on the page but the rules placed around the page as a border divide the space between the edge of the paper and the edge of the type into equal parts. This is considered a poor arrangement of the border.

Fig. 2

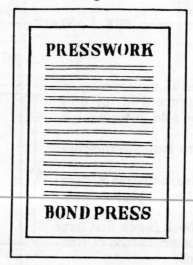

In Fig. 3 the rules are placed in a better location dividing the marginal spaces in good proportions. An approved method of finding the correct location for a border is to divide the marginal space on each side into eight parts and locate the border at the third division from the type. This, then, will make the space from the border to the edge of the paper five parts (5/8 of side margin) and the space between border and type three parts (3/8 of side margin). After the location of the side borders has been established, measure the distance from the type to the side borders and place the border at the top and bottom at the same distance.

Fig. 3

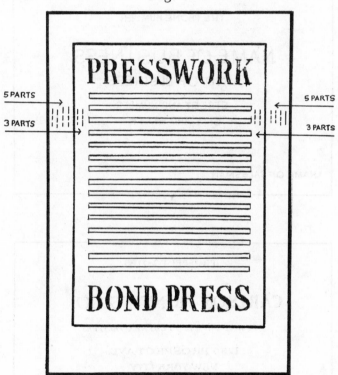

5 PARTS

3 PARTS

5 PARTS

3 PARTS

THE LAYOUT
COPY

SIZE: 4 in. by 6 in. deep
DISPLAY HEAD: Furniture
TEXT: The text will occupy a space 2 1/2 in. wide and 2 3/4 in.
     deep
SIGNATURE: Adams and Co.

DIRECTIONS

1. Arrange this furniture advertisement, making sure the margins are pleasingly proportioned.

2. Place a rule border around the page in the correct position, using a colored pencil when drawing the rule.

Unit 16   CONVENTIONAL BUSINESS CARDS

The business card has several uses, but its main function is to introduce a firm or company or perhaps a salesman or representative of the firm to another person or company. Therefore, it must look businesslike and be arranged to appeal to the person who sees it. The card must be attractive and easy to read so that the reader may grasp the entire message at one glance.

Fig. 1

THE PHONE NUMBER

NAME OF BUSINESS
KIND OF BUSINESS

STREET AND NUMBER
CITY AND STATE

NAME OF SALESMAN

Fig. 2

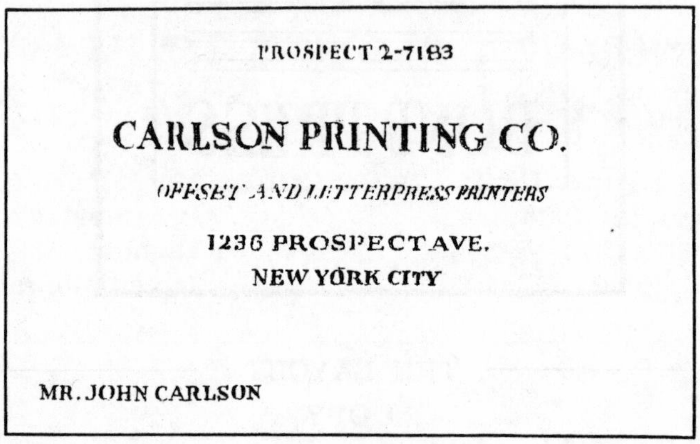

PROSPECT 2-7183

CARLSON PRINTING CO.

OFFSET AND LETTERPRESS PRINTERS

1236 PROSPECT AVE.
NEW YORK CITY

MR. JOHN CARLSON

Today some business cards are designed in the modern manner, but the greatest percentage are still arranged in the conventional style. A good standard conventional arrangement is illustrated in Figs. 1 and 2. The firm's name is just above the center and in the largest size type. Just below the name are the words describing the business, on the next line the street and number and below that the name of the city or town. If the name of a salesman or company representative is used, it is placed in the lower left-hand corner. If a telephone number is used, it may be placed near the top of the card. This style varies at times as the copy changes but as a general rule it is the standard procedure.

As business cards are small in size, the type sizes selected should not be too large. It is a common mistake made by printers to select a type size that is too large for the card. It is considered good practice to avoid using boldface type on business cards unless it is appropriate for the business. A card for a steel company or a trucking concern could appropriately use a boldface.

SIZES OF BUSINESS CARDS

Because of the many types of businesses and uses of the cards, there are several sizes and shapes. Among the printers, cards are frequently designated by numbers rather than dimensions. Some of the most common sizes are, in inches:

No. 63 - 3 7/8 by 2 3/8	No. 117 - 3 by 1 7/8
No. 55 - 4 1/2 by 2 1/2	No. 112 - 3 1/8 by 1 3/4
No. 48 - 4 1/2 by 2 5/8	No. 88 - 3 1/2 by 2
No. 32 - 5 1/2 by 3 1/4	No. 70 - 3 13/16 by 2 1/8

THE LAYOUT

COPY (A)	COPY (B)
SIZE: 4 1/2 in. by 2 1/2 in.	SIZE: 4 1/2 by 2 1/2
COPY: Parker Paper Co.	COPY: Morgan and Company
Papers for Printers	Ornamental Art Windows
Chicago, Ill.	Taunton, Mass.
G. J. Reed	James Morgan

DIRECTIONS

1. Select either copy (A) or copy (B) and arrange the business card in the conventional style.

2. Select a type you believe to be appropriate for the business and have the instructor check your selection.

3. Select the size type you plan to use for each line and have your selection checked by the instructor.

4. Make the finished layout and mark the sizes of type and the name of each type opposite each line.

Unit 17   TONE HARMONY

Tone harmony in the printed page is attained when the various elements such as type, illustrations, initials or borders have an even, uniform tone. When the tone is uniform, all the elements blend into an even gray or black. Then there is a harmony of tone which is one of the most important of the fundamentals of typography and design.

Type used for text or reading matter is usually designed to present an even gray tone, and if initials, illustrations and rules are to become a part of the page, they should be selected to harmonize with the type. If any of these elements were to have a darker tone, it would cause the printed page to appear "spotty." Dark spots are permissible only when used to emphasize certain parts of the page and even then in only a moderate degree.

In choosing initial letters to accompany type, care should be exercised to see that they are only slightly darker (if at all) than the type with which they are used.

In Fig. 1 the initial is too dark for the type, while in Fig. 2 it blends in with the type, giving an even gray tone.

THE FOLLOWING COULD be an actual conversation *today*. It, and others like it, would benefit our industry. "Here, Mr. Customer, is the printing you ordered, and here is the invoice for it."

Fig. 1

The same consideration should be given to the choice of ornaments and other decoration in relation to the body type. An ornament that is too heavy will stand out from the page instead of becoming a part of the composition. See Fig. 3 for an incorrect sample and Fig. 4 for a correct sample.

HERE IN America are the things which elsewhere in the world the nations stand in arms to conquer or to defend. A people with a long habit of freedom holds securely the space to live, a fertile soil, invested wealth, technical arts, everything a nation could need. Yet something is wanting.

Fig. 2

PHOTOGRAPHY TODAY

A TECHNICAL REVIEW

SMITH PUBLICATIONS
NEW YORK · LONDON · PARIS

Fig. 3

PHOTOGRAPHY TODAY

A TECHNICAL REVIEW

SMITH PUBLICATIONS
NEW YORK · LONDON · PARIS

Fig. 4

A layout containing cuts that are exceptionally dark in tone should be accompanied by type that is bold. Otherwise the cut would receive all of the attention and the type would not be read easily, if at all, (Fig. 5 and Fig. 6). Therefore, always attempt to have an even tone between cuts and type.

Fig. 5 *Cut attracts attention to itself. Type should be bolder.*

Fig. 6 *Cut and type have the same tone, aiding readability.*

--- THE LAYOUT ---

COPY (A)   Publication Advertisement

SIZE: 7 in. by 10 in. deep

CUT: 3 in. by 5 in. deep

DISPLAY HEAD: Mayonnaise to be proud of

CIRCULAR CUT: 1 1/2" in diameter

TEXT: You may use any amount of space you desire for the text. The copy would be written after the layout has been completed.

SIGNATURE: Wesson Oil

COPY (B)   Publication Advertisement

SIZE: 7 in. by 10 in. deep

DISPLAY HEAD: Why I Smoke Kool Cigarettes

CUT: 3 in. by 4 in. deep

TEXT: You may use any amount of space you desire for the text. The copy would be written after the layout has been completed.

CUT: Small cut of package of cigarettes

SIGNATURE: Kool Cigarettes

DIRECTIONS

1. Select either copy (A) or copy (B) and arrange the layout.

2. At the beginning of your text or reading matter in the layout, pencil in an initial and be sure it harmonizes with the text.

3. Be sure the type and cuts harmonize in tone.

4. Mark the type and type sizes on the finished layout.

Unit 18   BORDERS

Two types of borders are used by printers. One type is the plain rule border (Fig. 1) which comes in various point sizes, and the other is decorative borders that come in hundreds of various designs, a few of which are illustrated in Fig. 2.

Years ago, borders were used in books to enclose pages but today they are very seldom used for this purpose. They are, however, used in advertisements or around them. They should never be as important as the type, or attract the eye to such a great extent that the message is not read. If a person mentions that the border on a printed page is beautiful, it is sure proof that the border is interfering with the printed message.

Borders should not be used around the pages of books. Books that are to be read easily should not be dressed up in borders. Another mistake is to waste space on a border around a full-page or two-page advertisement. Such display has no competition in securing attention and, therefore, the border is not needed. There are times, of course, when a seasonal advertisement, such as an Easter advertisement, might feature a border of flowers, rabbits, etc. to advantage, but usually the full-page advertisement needs no border.

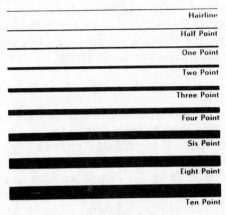

Fig. 1   *Rule Borders*

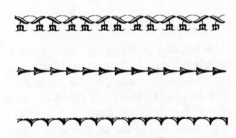

Fig. 2 *Decorative Borders*

A page advertising antique or decorative furniture would require a decorative border but an office furniture advertisement would undoubtedly use a single rule border to better advantage, as it would appear stiffer, colder, more businesslike. When in doubt, a plain rule border will be the best choice.

In the selection of a border, not only its appropriateness for the copy but also the class of readers for whom it is intended should be considered. A bank advertisement appealing to business men should have a straight line rule border, while a hosiery advertisement appealing to ladies would require a more decorative border.

The following rule will help you to select a border of the correct weight: "The border should be approximately the same weight as the upright strokes of the main display line" (Fig. 3). If a rule is heavier than the strokes of the display type (Fig. 4) the eye will be attracted to the border instead of to the message the type conveys. On a page where the type is very crowded, it is permissible in some instances to increase the weight of the border a little.

Besides having the same tone as the type, the border should harmonize in shape. If it contains curves, type should be selected that has curves in its design (Fig. 5). Some borders have been especially designed to be used with certain type faces. There are Caslon borders to be used with Caslon type, Bodoni borders for Bodoni type, etc.

A border printed in color should be heavier than if printed in black, as color tends to reduce the apparent weight or darkness. If borders are supplied that are too dark for the type when printed in black, printing in color will reduce the weight of the border and thereby assure a better harmony.

A single rule around an advertisement or page lacks variety. It gives the page a dull, commonplace appearance lacking appeal. A parallel rule (Fig. 6) or a contrast rule (Fig. 7) may improve this. Of the two the contrast rule is better because of the difference in the weight of the rules.

Fig. 3 *Type is easily read as the rule does not attract attention away from the type.*

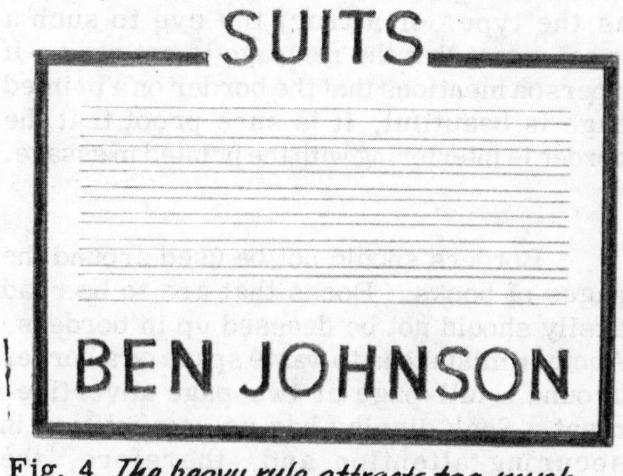

Fig. 4 *The heavy rule attracts too much attention making the type hard to read.*

Fig. 5 *Type and border harmonize as both have curves.*

Fig. 6 *Parallel Rule*

Fig. 7 *Contrast Rule*

When using the contrast rule, the lightest stroke should be on the inside towards the type (Fig. 8) as it leads the eye in towards the type. Fig. 9 shows an example of the effect given by having the thick line on the inside - it leads the eye out away from the type.

Some border designs tend to point in one direction and should never be used as in Fig. 10. They should always be arranged to point towards the type, not away from it (Fig. 11).

Certain parts of advertisements are sometimes set off by borders as a means of emphasis. If part of an advertisement is separated from the rest by a border, it is called an ad-box. If, in the reading columns of a newspaper or some other publication, a border surrounds some unusual news, it is known as a news-box. Last minute news or bulletins are often set in news-boxes on the front pages of newspapers.

RADIO
TODAY AND TOMORROW

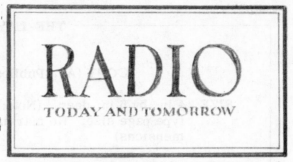

Fig. 8 *Thick stroke on the outside aids in leading the eye into the page*

RADIO
TODAY AND TOMORROW

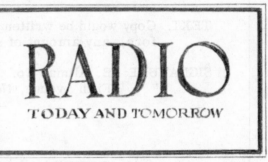

Fig. 9 *Contrast rule with the thick stroke on the inside leads the eye out of the page away from the type*

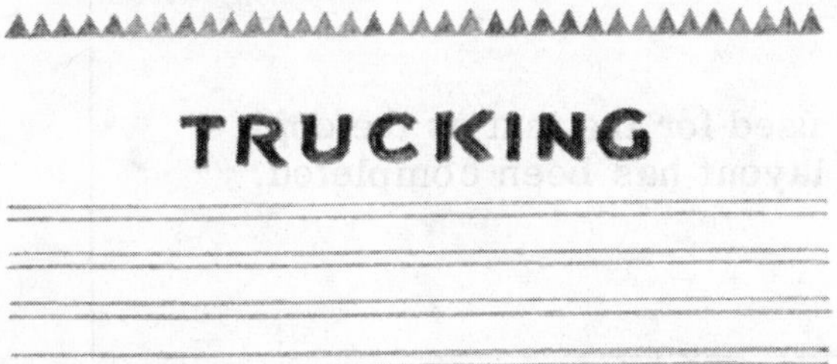
TRUCKING
TRIANGLE TRUCKERS

Fig. 10 *Border points out tending to make the reader's eye look out of the page.*

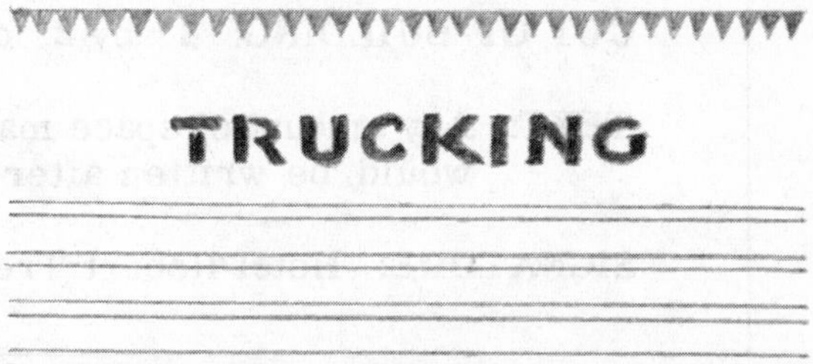
TRUCKING
TRIANGLE TRUCKERS

Fig. 11 *Border points into the page directing the reader's attention to the type*

THE LAYOUT

COPY (A)   Publication Advertisement

SIZE: 4 in. by 6 in. deep. (Note: These measurements are the type page size. No margin will be used inside these dimensions)

DISPLAY HEAD: Suede Oxfords

CUT OF SHOES: 1 3/4″ by 2 1/2″ deep

TEXT: Copy would be written after layout is completed; therefore, any amount of space may be used for the text.

SIGNATURE: B. Altman Co.
Fifth Avenue, New York

COPY (B)   Publication Advertisement

SIZE: 4 in. by 5 1/2 in. deep

DISPLAY HEAD: Newark's Smartest Address

CUT OF BUILDING: 1″ by 2″ deep

TEXT: Any amount of space may be used for the text as the copy would be written after the layout has been completed.

SIGNATURE: Hotel Robert Treat

DIRECTIONS

1. Select either Copy (A) or Copy (B) and make four thumbnail sketches, using a border in the layout.

2. After the thumbnail sketches have been checked by the instructor, make a finished layout of the one sketch selected.

3. When marking the layout for the compositor, make sure the size and style of border is indicated.

Unit 19   CONTRAST

One of the principles of design which finds wide application in putting punch into advertising display is that of contrast. Contrast is the use of type, illustrations and other elements of display in such a way that greater prominence is given to certain features through comparison either shown or implied. Contrast causes things to stand out and makes them instantly and strikingly apparent. A tall building among low ones or a flash of light at night compels attention by contrast with their surroundings or with what the mind usually associates with normal conditions.

In the same way punch is added to a printed piece by contrast. Notice how changing the type face in Fig. 2 has given the design more appeal than in Fig. 1.

THE LATEST MODELS

GRAY'S STYLE SHOP
NEW YORK CITY

Fig. 1

THE *Latest* MODELS

GRAY'S STYLE SHOP
NEW YORK CITY

Fig. 2

Fig. 3 shows some other ways by which contrast could be obtained in this same display line:

   (a) underscoring
   (b) larger size type
   (c) italic type
   (d) bold type

a. THE LATEST MODELS

b. THE LATEST MODELS

c. THE *LATEST* MODELS

d. THE **LATEST** MODELS

Fig. 3

In Fig. 3 the contrast makes the type talk or, in other words, it makes a person reading it accent certain words. Talking with type is much like speaking before an audience. A speaker that adds force to a few words is much more successful than one who shouts out every word. It is the same in display work, as one must avoid the use of too many display lines or groups as well as too many different sizes of type. It is much more effective to accent only one or two words as in Fig. 2 rather than several words.

THE LAYOUT

COPY (A)   Publication Advertisement

SIZE: 7 in. by 10 in. deep

DISPLAY HEAD: In a cigarette it's taste

LARGE CUT: 3 1/2 in. by 5 in. deep

SMALL CUT: Cut of package of cigarettes. Trace the package the same size as the photograph which is supplied.

TEXT: The copy would be written after the layout has been completed; therefore, no definite amount of space is to be saved for the body.

SIGNATURE: Chesterfield

COPY (B)   Publication Advertisement

SIZE: 7 in. by 10 in. deep

DISPLAY HEAD: Color for Spring

LARGE CUT: 3 in. by 4 in. deep

SMALL CUT: 2 in. by 1 1/2 in. deep

TEXT: You may use any amount of space for the text you desire. The copy would be written after the layout has been completed.

SIGNATURE: Creations by Saks Fifth Avenue

DIRECTIONS

1. Select either copy (A) or copy (B) and make at least four thumbnail sketches to be submitted to the instructor.

2. When making the thumbnail sketches study the copy and select the words or groups of words which should be accented and illustrate the method of accenting in the sketches.

3. After the sketches have been checked by the instructor and one selected, make the finished layout.

Unit 20   POINTING DEVICES

Pointing devices of various types have been employed for years to lead the eye in advertisements. Not many years ago the obvious arrow and the hand with a pointing forefinger, known to printers as the "index," were the pointing devices that were popular. They were almost the only shortcuts employed by early advertising designers to lead the eye to the most important features of the display.

It is necessary for the layout man to direct the eye to the most important unit in the layout. He may wish to direct attention to the coupon, to the signature, to the product or to emphasize the display head. Today the arrow and pointing finger are very seldom used, but other methods of direction and emphasis have found their way into printing design. One of the most popular is to utilize an illustration of the product itself to point to some particular unit. One of the most outstanding instances of such treatment can be found in advertisements of such items as fountain pens and pencils. Articles of this type, like the arrow or "index," can be arranged to point because of their shape.

Fig. 1 *POOR — Shoe points out of the layout leading the eye away from the type. The figure is walking out of the advertisement leading the eye away from the type*

Fig. 2 *GOOD — Shoe points towards the signature. The figure is walking into the advertisement directing attention to the type.*

When cuts (or illustrations) are placed in the layout, have them point in the direction the eye should travel (Fig. 2). Have the figures or objects looking or heading in the direction the eyes of the reader should move. They should also head or face into the advertisement, not out of it. Advertisements with illustrations that are pointing to the right look best on a left-hand page so that they will appear to be heading into the publication.

THE LAYOUT

COPY (A) Publication Advertisement

SIZE: 4 3/4 in. by 12 in. deep

DISPLAY HEAD: Chelton Wingflow

CUT: Trace cut of pen supplied by instructor.

SUBHEAD: The finest pen made

CUTS: 3 cuts each 1 in. by 3/4 in. deep

TEXT: No definite space required for text

SIGNATURE: Chelton Pens

COPY (B) Publication Advertisement

SIZE: 7 in. by 10 in. deep

DISPLAY HEAD: Gives you tailored writing

CUT: 2 1/2 in. by 3 in. deep

SUBHEAD: Four New Features

CUT: Cut of pen to be supplied by instructor

TEXT: No definite amount of space required for the text

SIGNATURE: Eversharp Tailored Writing

DIRECTIONS

1. Select either Copy (A) or (B).

2. Make four thumbnail sketches of copy selected and have them checked by the instructor.

3. Make a finished layout of the sketch selected and mark the layout for the compositor.

Unit 21   DIRECTING EYE MOVEMENT

As every moving picture or stage production has its star, every layout should have its outstanding unit or center of interest.

Before starting sketches for a layout, the designer should study the copy and select the most important unit. The copy usually gives the layout man a hint as to the most important unit. It may be the picture of the product, name of the product or some person or place the copy may be referring to. Whatever the layout man selects as the important unit should be placed in the layout in a position that would be noticed by a busy person who had time only to glance at the page, as well as by the person who could spend considerable time reading it.

Through research work conducted by advertising agencies and large printing plants, it has been found that the eye usually enters a page at the left side near the top. Undoubtedly this is because readers have always started to read from that corner on a page and the eye has formed the habit of looking there the minute it glances at a sheet of paper.

From this point, it has been found, the eye leaps to the focal point of the page (Fig. 1) and then, unless held by something interesting, passes downward and to the right passing out of the page at approximately the place where the thumb and fingers are usually getting ready to turn the page. (Follow arrow in Fig. 1.) The focal point, which is just above the center of the page, has been found to be the best area in which to locate the most important unit of the layout.

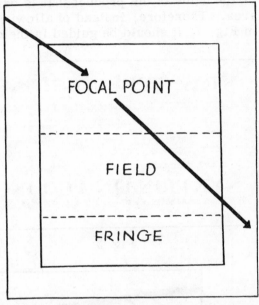

Fig. 1 *Arrow shows the direction the eye normally passes over a page unless guided by the arrangement of the units of the layout.*

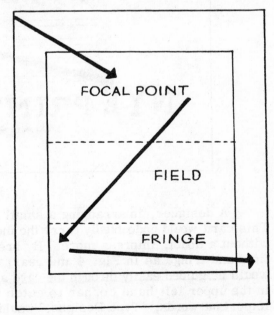

Fig. 2 – *Arrow shows one of the methods of directing the eye through the page*

Just below the focal point is an area of less attraction which we may call the field (Fig. 1). In this area it is necessary to hold the eye of the reader after leaving the focal area so that the person will not leave the page immediately. This is accomplished by using interesting cuts, subheads or text matter. It is essential that the reader's eye be guided through this field to the fringe (Fig. 2). The signature, or the name of the product that is being advertised, is usually located in the fringe area. Therefore, instead of allowing the eye to pass through the advertisement as in Fig. 1, it should be guided in the direction the arrow travels in Fig. 2.

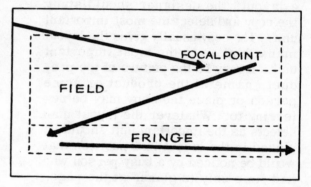

Fig. 3

Fig. 4

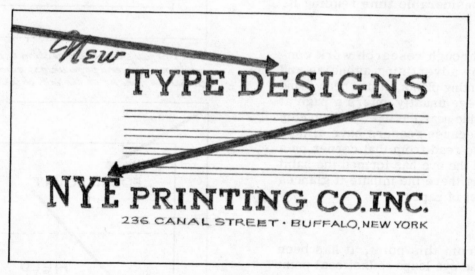

Fig. 5

A designer, in arranging a small mailing card, might arrange it as in Fig. 3. This card would undoubtedly carry the message to some, but if changed slightly would, without a doubt, impress more. By breaking up the card and finding its focal point, field and fringe as in Fig. 4 and rearranging the copy into these divisions, the eye would be guided easily through the card as in Fig. 5. The word "New" would be placed in the upper left hand corner to catch the eye as it entered the page and the most important words, "Type Designs," would be located in the focal point. As the eye left the focal point it would be attracted to the word "NYE" which would be set larger and would complete the reading of the line.

This same method of directing the eye can be employed in more complicated arrangements as Fig. 6. Notice how the eye travels through this advertisement.

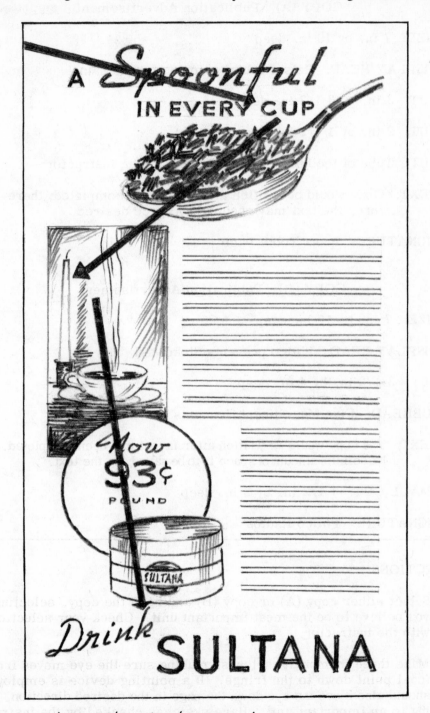

Fig. 6 *Arrows show the direction the reader's eyes will travel through the advertisement*

THE LAYOUT

COPY (A) Publication Advertisement

SIZE: 7 in. by 10 in. deep

DISPLAY HEAD: He's a dental cripple just the same

CUT: 3 in. by 3 1/2 in. deep

CUT: 2 in. by 1 1/2 in. deep

CUT: Tube of toothpaste to be supplied by the instructor

TEXT: Copy would be written after layout is completed; there-fore, the text may occupy any space desired.

SIGNATURE: Ipana Tooth Paste

COPY (B) Publication Advertisement

SIZE: 7 in. by 10 in. deep

DISPLAY HEAD: Philco presents Stokowski

CUT: 3 1/2 in. by 4 in. deep

SUBHEAD: Five Magnificent Concerts

TEXT: The copy would be written after layout has been completed. No definite amount of space is to be saved for the text.

SMALL CUT: 1 1/2 in. by 2 in. deep

SIGNATURE: Philco Radios

DIRECTIONS

1. Select either copy (A) or copy (B) and read the copy, selecting what you believe to be the most important unit. Check your selection with with the instructor.

2. Make three thumbnail sketches, making sure the eye moves from the focal point down to the fringe. If a pointing device is employed, it should also move the eye down the page in the desired direction, pointing to an important unit. Have sketches checked by the instructor.

3. Make the finished layout and mark the layout for the compositor.

Unit 22   GROUPING DISPLAY LINES

In many cases, the display heads are too long to set in one complete line and the layout man finds it necessary to group them into two, three or more lines. Poorly trained men will distort them into various formations and angles which make the copy hard to read. A skilled designer will arrange the head to form either an inverted pyramid (Fig. 1), squared effect (Fig. 2), drop line (Fig. 3) or long and short line arrangement (Fig. 4). These groups are the most common and most useful arrangements employed by layout men.

The inverted pyramid (Fig. 1) with the longest line at the top and the following lines gracefully tapering to a point is a widely used and generally accepted form. As the inverted pyramid points downward, it leads the eye into the page and points down in the direction a person naturally looks or reads.

The regular pyramid (Fig. 5) points upward and tends to lead the eye out of the display; therefore, it should not be used unless there is an illustration or group placed above the shape.

The dropline arrangement must have about the same number of characters in each line, just as the squared group and the group with each line moved to the right as in Fig. 3. This is a very popular arrangement and one that is easily read.

The most popular, easiest to set and one of the most pleasing arrangements is that in which the lines are permitted to make what they will (Fig. 4). This long and short line arrangement seems natural and is very easy to read. In using the long and short line method, the lines are centered with the longest line in the display placed at or near the top. If possible, the shortest line should not be placed next to the longest line. In Fig. 4 the longest line is the first one and the shortest the last.

Fig. 1

THE BEST BUY
IS HERE
TODAY

Fig. 2

THE ART OF
LETTERPRESS
ON DISPLAY

Fig. 3

THE ART OF
LETTERPRESS
ON DISPLAY

Fig. 4

For Old-time Chocolate Flavor

the CHOC Brand

Cannot be Excelled

in Any Way

Fig. 5

TODAY
THE BEST BUY
IS ON DISPLAY HERE

The oblong or squared effect should not be used unless the copy falls naturally into a squared arrangement without letterspacing a part of it. In Fig. 6 the words have been distorted in order to square the group.

One line should not be interspaced or letterspaced and another set solid. If one line of a group is letterspaced, the other lines should be also.

If the lines of display do not naturally form a pleasing group, do not try to force them into a shape as in Fig. 6 but let them set naturally into a pleasing group as in Fig. 7.

The display head usually carries a message in itself. When it is broken up into several lines, the breaks should be made so that each line makes sense. If it is broken in this way, the reader will get the thought more quickly and clearly.

Fig. 8 is an example of a group broken into lines that do not make sense and in Fig. 9 the same group is rearranged to be easily read and clearly understood.

BOOTH
PRINTING
Fig. 6   # CORP.

Type should not be forced into a shape by letterspacing part of the group as in Fig 6. Type should be allowed to naturally set into a shape as in Fig. 7.

BOOTH
PRINTING
Fig. 7   # CORP.

For Old-time Chocolate

Flavor the CHOC.

Brand cannot be

Excelled in Any Way

Fig. 8   *The lines are broken so that they do not make sense*

For Old-time Chocolate Flavor

The CHOC Brand

Cannot be Excelled

in Any Way

Fig. 9   *The lines are broken so as to make sense when reading.*

```
┌─────────────────────── THE  LAYOUT ───────────────────────┐
│                                                            │
│              COPY (A)   Publication Advertisement          │
│                                                            │
│    SIZE:  24 picas by 72 picas deep (Note:  This is the type page size. │
│           No margin will be inside these measurements.)    │
│                                                            │
│    DISPLAY HEAD:  To work with father, to town with mother, to │
│                   play with sister                         │
│                                                            │
│    TEXT:  Copy would be written after completion of layout; there- │
│           fore, no definite space has to be left for the text. │
│                                                            │
│    CUT:  24 picas by 16 picas deep                         │
│                                                            │
│    CUTS:  Two cuts, each 11 picas by 7 picas deep          │
│                                                            │
│    SIGNATURE:  Chevrolet, quality and service              │
│                                                            │
│                                                            │
│              COPY (B)   Publication Advertisement          │
│                                                            │
│    SIZE:  Type page, 24 picas by 72 picas deep (Note:  No margin │
│           inside these measurements)                       │
│                                                            │
│    DISPLAY HEAD:  Snoozers, a modern idea in pajamas       │
│                                                            │
│    CUT:  18 picas by 30 picas deep                         │
│                                                            │
│    CUTS:  Two cuts, each 6 picas by 8 picas deep           │
│                                                            │
│    TEXT:  No definite amount of space for the text.  Copy would be │
│           written after layout is completed.               │
│                                                            │
│    SUBHEAD:  Now only $5 a pair                            │
│                                                            │
│    SIGNATURE:  Capper and Capper                           │
│                Fifth Avenue, New York                      │
│                                                            │
└────────────────────────────────────────────────────────────┘
```

DIRECTIONS

1. Select either Copy (A) or Copy (B).

2. Make four thumbnail sketches of your selection, making sure your
    display heads are arranged in pleasing groups. Submit sketches to
    the instructor.

3. Make a finished layout of the sketch selected and mark it for the com-
    positor.

Unit 23   CONVENTIONAL TICKETS

Tickets are printed on both white and colored stock. Some printers buy tickets that are already cut to size and corners rounded, while others buy sheets of bristol board in large sizes such as 22 1/2" by 28 1/2" and cut the tickets to the desired size. There are standard ticket sizes, such as No. 117 - 3" × 1 5/8" and No. 88 - 3 3/8" × 1 15/16", but when cutting his own tickets the printer usually selects a size that is appropriate for the job. A ticket should not be square, or too long and narrow, but a good proportion such as the 2" × 3" or 3" × 5".

Fig. 1

Fig. 2

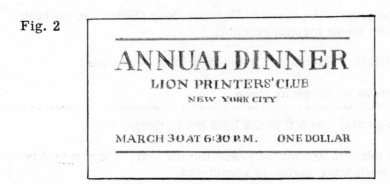

When designing tickets, the size of the type is governed by the size of the ticket and the amount of copy. As tickets are small in size, large sizes of type would look out of place. Either caps or caps and lower case may be used and at times a line of italic is appropriate.

The copy should be studied before arranging and lines that read together should be grouped together. For example, in Fig. 1 the name of the affair (ANNUAL DINNER), the society holding the affair (LION PRINTERS' CLUB) and the location of the club (NEW YORK CITY) should be arranged in a single group. The groups of type should be well shaped as explained in the last unit and the most important line or group placed above the center at the focal point.

Tickets may be arranged with a border surrounding the copy as in Fig. 1 or with a border strip at the top and bottom (Fig. 2) and in many other ways. If a border is used, it should always be placed closer to the type than the edge of the paper. The nature of the copy will aid in regulating the type of arrangement.

THE LAYOUT

COPY (A) Ticket

SIZE: 3 1/2 in. by 2 in. deep

COPY: Annual Automobile Show
      Hartford State Armory
      Broad Street
      November 25 to 28
      $1.25

COPY (B) Ticket

SIZE: 3 1/2 in. by 2 in. deep

COPY: Annual Spring Meeting
      Printers' Association
      Hotel Taft
      April 10 at 6:30 P. M.
      Three Dollars

DIRECTIONS

1. Select either Copy (A) or Copy (B).

2. Make thumbnail sketches of the copy selected.

3. Select the better sketch without the aid of the instructor and make the finished layout.

4. Mark the type sizes and the name of the type on the layout.

Unit 24   APPROPRIATENESS IN DISPLAY

Before starting to work, the layout man should always study the copy and consider the type of article to be advertised as well as the type of person who would be interested in the product. A man is very seldom interested in advertisements designed to sell cosmetics or silk stockings, and few women are interested in the buying of machinery, trucks or tractors. Every advertisement designed should be made to appeal to the people who buy the article advertised. The selection of type, illustrations, ornament and border should conform to the article it is meant to sell.

In order to design an advertisement appropriate to the article advertised, thought should be given to the selection of the proper type, illustrations and border. For an advertisement which is to sell an article to women, an air of femininity should distinguish it. In order to express daintiness, or femininity, the layout might become somewhat ornamental, but it should not become so to such an extent as to interfere with legibility. For display lines of such an advertisement the type selected should be of a delicate character and should be surrounded by white space so as to give the lines prominence (Figs. 1 and 2). The border and illustration should not be bold, or dark in tone, but should harmonize with the type design selected (Figs. 1 and 2).

Fig. 1 *Too bold and masculine to appeal to women. This bold type and border would be appropriate for a steel or truck advertisement.*

Fig. 2 *Appropriate style for women. Free use of white space and a good harmony of type and border. This style would appeal to women.*

If an advertisement is to appeal to a prosperous business man, it should be dignified (Fig. 3). In order to express dignity, the border should be a plain rule and the type plain, clean-cut, legible and medium in weight. The formal type of layout, using considerable white space, would aid in expressing dignity.

In advertisements displaying trucks (Fig. 5), tractors, iron, steel, brick, etc. a suggestion of ruggedness should enter into the layout. The type, border and illustrations should be bold to signify strength and durability.

Always decide, before starting a layout, the character of the article to be advertised and the type of people it should appeal to. Each article advertised has its appropriate style and treatment, and this varies even with the different grades of the same article. In the case of automobiles, the limousine requires a different treatment from that of the truck.

Fig. 3 – In order to appeal to the business man plain border and type face should be used. Formal balance and the free use of white space would also help.

Fig. 4

Fig. 5

THE LAYOUT

COPY (A)   Publication Advertisement

SIZE: 7 in. by 10 in. deep

DISPLAY HEAD: Toncan, the reliable steel

CUT: 18 picas by 21 picas deep

SUBHEAD: Safe with Toncan

TEXT: No definite space required for text

SIGNATURE: U. S. Steel Co.

COPY (B)   Publication Advertisement

SIZE: 7 in. by 10 in. deep

DISPLAY HEAD: Charm in Silverware

CUT: 2 in. by 4 in. deep

CUT: 1 1/2 in. by 2 in. deep

TEXT: No definite space required for text

SIGNATURE: Homes Silver Co.

DIRECTIONS

1. Make thumbnail sketches of either Copy (A) or (B), making sure that the layout is appropriate.

2. Have the instructor check the sketches and aid in the selection of the most appropriate one.

3. Make the finished layout and mark it completely.

Unit 25   CONVENTIONAL LETTERHEADS

The purpose of the letterhead is to carry a business message from a firm to the persons with whom the company corresponds. A great deal of consideration and thought should be given the selection of type and arrangement of the letterhead. If it makes a good appearance, it will give the reader a favorable impression of the company.

Business letterheads are usually printed on a paper called bond. This paper is made with a very hard finish which makes an excellent surface for writing with pen and ink. The common letterhead sizes are 8 1/2″ × 5 1/2″, 8 1/2″ × 7 1/4″, 7 1/4″ × 10 1/2″ and 8 1/2″ × 11″. The last named size is the most commonly used.

The sizes of type used on a letterhead vary from 6-point to 30-point. Type larger than 30-point is very seldom used. More than one family of type should not be used unless, as explained farther along in this unit, there is a very good reason. The type should be arranged into one group, if possible, and a great deal of thought should be given the shape of the group. The type should be arranged in either a squared shape, inverted pyramid or long and short line group. The group should be centered near the top of the page.

In arranging the group, the name of the concern should be at the top, the name of the business next and then address. The name is usually the most important and should be set in the largest size type (Fig. 1). There are some times, however, when the product should be displayed more than the name. If branch offices, cable address, telephone or other subordinate material must be included, it should be placed in small light-faced type across the very top of the page or arranged in two small balancing groups on each side of the center display. This material should be kept small and light so as to fall into the background.

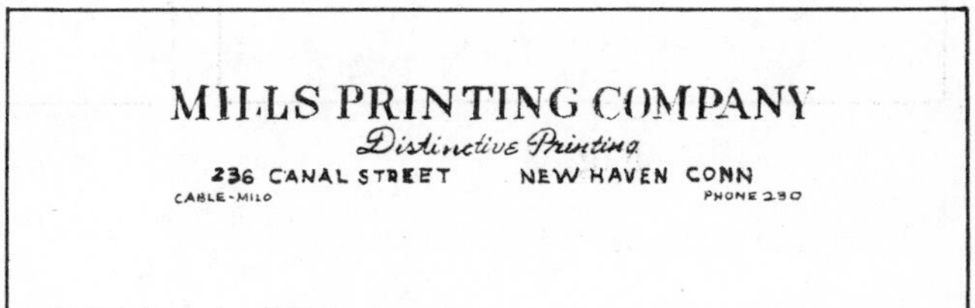

MILLS PRINTING COMPANY
Distinctive Printing
236 CANAL STREET   NEW HAVEN CONN
CABLE-MILO   PHONE 230

Fig. 1

Conventional letterheads should not have the main group arranged in a pyramid pointing up as in Fig. 2. With the longest line arranged at the head, as in Fig. 3, the group points toward the letter itself, which is the direction in which the eye should travel.

THE MACON & JONES CO.
Printers
LAYOUT · ART · COPY · LETTERPRESS AND OFFSET PRINTING
NEW YORK   CHICAGO

THE MACON AND JONES COMPANY
Printers
LAYOUT · ART · COPY · LETTERPRESS AND OFFSET PRINTING
NEW YORK · CHICAGO

Fig. 2	Fig. 3

THE LAYOUT

COPY (A) Letterhead

SIZE: 8 1/2 in. × 11 in. deep

COPY: Howland Hardware Company
Wholesale Building Supplies
271 Main Street
Spencer, Ohio

COPY (B) Letterhead

SIZE: 8 1/2 in. × 11 in. deep

COPY: The Hood and Stokes Company
Offset and Lithographic Printing
New York City
Layout, Art Work, Printing, Binding

DIRECTIONS

1. Select Copy (A) or Copy (B) and arrange the letterhead, completing the entire finished layout before showing it to the instructor.

Unit 26   ANATOMY OF A BOOK
(Preliminary Section)

Besides designing advertising printing, the printer has to be able to plan and design books.   In designing books, the layout man is not so free to use his original arrangements because there are firmly established rules that have been used for years and are still in use.   Since book publishers follow these traditional standards and rules, the student should become acquainted with them.

PARTS OF A BOOK

Every book consists of three major divisions:

The Preliminaries - This includes the title and other pages that are used for identification, explanation and preparation. These pages are placed in the front of the book

The Text - The text consists of the chapters containing the reading matter.

The Reference - This consists of some or all of the following: appendix, supplement, bibliography, glossary, vocabulary or index.   These are placed in the back of the book.

THE PRELIMINARY PART OF A BOOK

The preliminary section of a book is composed of the following pages:

Sequence of Pages	Name of Page	Page Number
Page 1	Book Half Title	Not printed
Page 2	Publisher's Agencies	Not printed
(Frontispiece may follow publisher's agencies but usually is not counted)		
Page 3	Title Page	Not printed
Page 4	Copyright	Not printed
Page 5	Dedication	Not printed
Page 6	Blank page	Not printed
Page 7	Preface (First use of folio)	Folio printed - vii
Next right-hand page	Table of Contents	Folio printed - ix
Next right-hand page	List of illustrations	Folio printed - xi
Next right-hand page	Introduction	Folio printed - xiii

All books do not follow the page numbering as shown in this example.   Some books have no publisher's agencies; some have no dedication page and others contain a frontispiece preceding the title page.

The half title, title and dedication pages are all display matter and should be set in the same family of type and treated the same. It is best to use no periods at the ends of lines on these pages and to punctuate as little as possible.

In most books the preliminary pages are numbered with Roman numerals, often times set in lower case; for example, vi, vii, viii, ix. The page number, or folio as the printer calls it, does not appear on the display pages or any other very open page. Pages which are not numbered, such as half title, publisher's agencies, title page, copyright and dedication are counted, however, in the preliminary page numbering. The Roman numerals usually appear first on the preface page, at the foot, about a pica below the type in the center.

BOOK HALF TITLE

Usually the book half title is the first printed page in the book. In some books an announcement or advertising card may appear first or, if the book is only one of several in a group or series of books, a series half title may appear before the book half title. Only the name of the book is printed on the half title page, and it should be placed in the focal point on a right-hand page. Half titles are also used before each part of the text when it is broken into parts and sometimes before each chapter.

PUBLISHER'S AGENCIES

If the publishers have agents or representatives in foreign countries who sell or distribute the book, these agents are listed on the back of the half title page. The publisher's agencies are set in a small size type and the group should be placed in the focal area of the page.

FRONTISPIECE

The frontispiece does not appear in all books but, if used, should be placed on the next left-hand page following the publisher's agencies and facing the title page. This page usually contains an illustration, map or diagram that deals with the title of the book.

TITLE PAGE

The title page follows on the next right-hand page after the frontispiece. If the frontispiece is not used, it will follow the preceding page which is the publisher's agencies. The title of the book, the name of the author and the name of the publishing house with its address are necessary elements of title page composition. The publisher's trade mark or some other ornament is usually added as an embellishment. Any further information on the page complicates the problem of the designer. Sometimes the date of publication may appear in connection with the publisher's name, though it must also appear with the copyright notice on the following page.

COPYRIGHT NOTICE

The copyright notice appears on the back of the title page, often with a statement giving the date of publication, the date of reprinting and of the new editions. The copyright is secured from the federal government and is a type of protection for the author's material in the book. If all or parts of the material found in a copyrighted book are used without the author's or publisher's permission, penalties against the offender can be inflicted. To be legally copyrighted, the notice must be placed on the back of the title page or on the title page. Near the bottom of the copyright page the printer's imprint is placed when used.

The copyright should be set in a very small size type and placed in the focal area of the page. The printer's imprint in the same size type as the copyright or smaller is placed near the foot of the page.

THE DEDICATION

Some authors dedicate their books to friends or relatives. This dedication, when used, should be placed on the right-hand page following the copyright notice. The dedication usually consists of only two or three lines and should be placed about 3/8 down the page in the focal area. The page following the dedication is always blank.

THE PREFACE

The preface contains the author's formal statement of the purpose of the book, his instructions as to its use and sometimes his acknowledgements, which may be a separate item if there are many. This preface should be placed on the next right-hand page following the dedication. The word "Preface" should be used as the head and should be sunken or set down about 3 or 4 picas below the top margin of the type page. It should be set in the same size and family of type as the text section of the book. In early books the preface was set in italics and this style is still used at times. The folio (page number) makes its first appearance on this page and should be a Roman numeral. The preceding pages are counted but not numbered so the preface page will not be numbered page i but perhaps v, vi or vii, depending upon the number of pages that have preceded it. The folio is placed at the foot of the page about a pica below the type in the center.

TABLE OF CONTENTS

The table of contents should begin on the next right-hand page after the preface and is usually set in a size of type smaller than the text. It should be a brief outline of the contents of the book, omitting the pages up to and including the table of contents. It should list the chapter headings and, if subheads are given, their relation to the main headings should be shown by the use of indention, grouping or a smaller size type. Subheads should be set to hand indented under each chapter title. The line "Table of Contents" is used as the head and should be sunken or set down from the top of the page the same distance as the word "Preface." The folio should appear on this page and all of the following pages.

LIST OF ILLUSTRATIONS

The list of illustrations should match the table of contents in general style. This page lists the pictures, maps, diagrams, etc. that the book contains. The titles used in the list need not read exactly like the legends (titles under the cuts) under the illustrations. If the legend is long, a shortened form that is not misleading may be used.

INTRODUCTION

The introduction usually explains the position taken by the author toward his subject and toward other writers. These pages should be the same as the preface in style, using "Introduction" as the head. It should start on a right-hand page following the "List of illustrations."

ASSIGNMENT PROBLEMS

A. On a separate sheet of paper answer the following questions

B. When the questions have been answered, give the paper to the instructor who will check the answers.

1. What are the three parts of a book?

2. What is the name of the first printed page in a book?

3. What is the folio?

4. Should the folio be placed at the head or the foot of the title page?

5. On which page would you place the printer's imprint?

6. On what page does the copyright law require the copyright notice to be placed?

7. On what page does the folio first appear?

8. What is the frontispiece?

9. What type of numerals should be used in the preliminary section of a book?

10. What pages should use a sunken head?

11. What is the difference between the book half title and the title page?

12. If the dedication contains only two lines, where should it be placed on the page?

13. What is placed on the back of the dedication page?

14. Should the reading matter in the preface be set in the same size type as the text of the book or smaller?

15. List in order the pages of the preliminary section of a book.

Unit 27   ANATOMY OF A BOOK
(Text and Reference)

TEXT

The first chapter in the text section of a book should start on a right-hand page and should have a chapter number or head. The title of the chapter may be the same size as the chapter number or smaller and set in the same size and family of type and sunken in the same way as the heads of the preface and introduction pages of the preliminary section. The folio is centered at the bottom of the first page of each chapter, sometimes in brackets, about a pica below the type page. Paging the book with Arabic figures (1, 2, 3) begins with the text of the book.

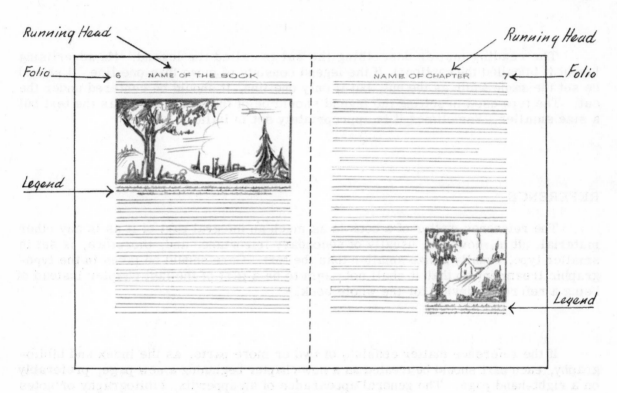

Fig. 1

The margins of the text pages are arranged as explained in Unit 14, Block I. At the top of each page, in the marginal space, about a pica above the text matter is a line called the running head (Fig. 1). This line is usually set in caps or small caps of the type being used in the text. For running heads of a book the commonest usage prescribes the name of the book on the left-hand page and the name of the chapter on the right-hand page. The folio usually appears on the same line with the running head at the outer margin, flush with the type page (Fig. 1). Placing the chapter head at the top of the page at the beginning of each chapter forces the folio to be moved to the foot. When the folio is at the foot of the page it is called the drop folio. There are, however, many variations of this form of handling the running head and folio.

In arranging text pages, the positioning of type matter and illustrations should be carefully planned for balance. Where but one illustration is to appear on a page it should be placed above the center. If it is narrower than the page and has type matter down one side, it should be placed next to the outer rather than the inner margin (Fig. 1). In case two cuts are balanced on opposite pages, remember that the larger cut should be placed nearer the center and the smaller one farther away (Fig. 1).

White space on all sides of a cut should appear to be equal. The width of each space should be governed by the general character of the page. If the text is set in a large size type, well leaded, with wide margins, there should be enough space around the cut to give it an uncrowded appearance.

The reading matter describing the cut is called the legend. (In advertising layout it is called the caption.) If the legend consists of more than one line, it should be set the same width as the cut, but if only one line, it should be centered under the cut. The type used in setting the legend should be of the same family as the text but a size smaller. Sometimes it is appropriately set in italic.

REFERENCE

The reference matter of a book is as much an integral part of it as is any other material. It is, however, usually of secondary importance and, therefore, is set in smaller type, usually a size smaller than the text. Care should be taken in the typographic treatment so that it shall not seem to be a part of the last chapter instead of being a reference device for the whole book.

If the reference matter consists of two or more parts, as the index and bibliography, each part should be treated as a new chapter beginning a new page, preferably on a right-hand page. The general appearance of an appendix, bibliography or notes is similar to that of the pages of the text, but a glossary, vocabulary or an index consists of short lines and these are usually set in two or more columns.

ASSIGNMENT PROBLEMS

A. On a separate sheet of paper complete the following sentences.

B. When the sentences have been completed, have the instructor check the answers.

1. The three parts of a book are the text, the references and the _____ sections.

2. In the text of the book the name of the chapter is placed on the _____ hand page in the running head.

3. The descriptive matter underneath a cut is called the _____

4. The reference section of a book is set in a _____ size type than the text.

5. _____ numbers are used for the folio in the text section of a book while _____ numbers are used in the preliminary section.

6. White space around a cut should always be _____

7. When the folio is placed at the foot of the page it is called the _____

8. The pages in the preliminary section of the book are the title page, table of contents, list of illustrations, introduction, publisher's agencies and _____, _____ , _____ , _____ , _____ .

9. In the preliminary section of a book the folio first appears on the _____ page.

10. According to the federal copyright law, the copyright notice must be placed on the back of the _____ page.

Unit 28 TITLE PAGES

In a book, undoubtedly the most difficult page to arrange is the title page. The purpose of this page is to give an idea of the contents of the book and serve as an introduction to the text. To fulfill this purpose, the page usually contains:

1. The name of the book
2. The author's name
3. Some descriptive matter
4. The name and address of the publishers

The designer has more freedom in arranging this page than any other in a book, but should not allow himself to become obsessed with the desire to produce something different or original. If we remember that the copy on title pages is always different, we can see that this allows the designer to arrange title pages so that no two jobs will look identical.

As there are only a few lines of copy on a title page, the designer is apt to spread out the lines to give a separated appearance to the page (Fig. 1). The lines that read together and are related should be grouped together, and the fewer groups formed the better (Fig. 2).

EUROPEANS

A STORY OF THE
PEOPLE OF EUROPE

BY

JOHN C. GILL

CORRESPONDENT FOR

THE NEW YORK PRESS

NEW YORK

ACE PUBLISHING CO.

1942

EUROPEANS
A STORY OF THE PEOPLE OF EUROPE

BY

JOHN C. GILL
CORRESPONDENT FOR THE
NEW YORK PRESS

NEW YORK
ACE PUBLISHING CO.
1942

Fig. 1    Fig. 2

Years ago, the title page was embellished with decorative borders and orna- ments, but today simplicity is the keynote of all printing, so plain borders and simple ornaments are preferred to fancy designs. Plain type designs should also be selected and the type used should be of the same family as that employed throughout the book.

When designing title pages, there are several facts that the designer should keep in mind and consider. In the first place, the title page is a right-hand page; therefore, the left-hand margin at the gutter would be narrowest, head a little wider, outside still wider and the foot widest. The weight should be placed above the center of the title page. This is accomplished by placing the largest group of type and the longest lines above the center (Fig. 4). If the weight were below the center, it would appear to the eye to be off balance (Fig. 3). Therefore, its construction should be just the opposite of a tall building which is bulky or large at the bottom and small at the top. A title page should be large at the top and small at the bottom.

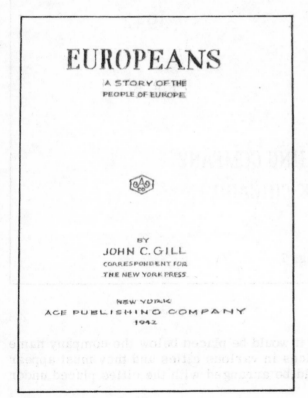

Fig. 3

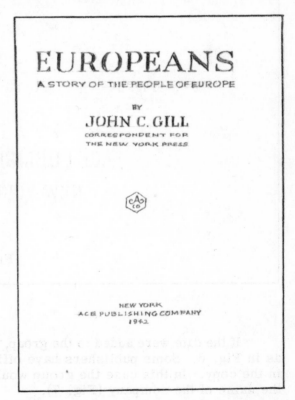

Fig. 4

As mentioned before, the type selected should be of the same family as the other pages in the book. A title page should not be overdisplayed, so large sizes of type should be used sparingly. The name of the book is usually in the largest size, author's name second and the other lines considerably smaller. Some designers claim that it is safest to set a page either all caps or all lower case. This is a very safe rule to follow, but at times when a great deal of descriptive copy is on the page, one style might become tiresome to the reader, whereas a page set partly in caps and partly in lower case would have a little more variety.

The publisher's name and address at the foot of the page are arranged in a traditional style which is still correct today. If the name of the publishing company and one city is used as the address, it is set as in Fig. 5, with the city placed above the address.

NEW YORK
ACE PUBLISHING COMPANY

Fig. 5

NEW YORK
ACE PUBLISHING COMPANY
1942

Fig. 6

ACE PUBLISHING COMPANY
NEW YORK·CHICAGO

Fig. 7

If the date were added to the group, it would be placed below the company name as in Fig. 6. Some publishers have offices in various cities and they must appear in the copy. In this case the group would be arranged with the cities placed under the name of the company (Fig. 7).

When the title page is fairly open, an ornament is quite often placed between the large group at the head of the page and the small group at the foot. The ornament should harmonize with the type in tone and also be appropriate for the subject. For example, an ornament using a decorative bird as the motif would not be appropriate in a book on Presswork. Instead, some design related to printing should be used. If an ornament that harmonizes with the subject cannot be secured, perhaps one that harmonizes with the type may be used. Several type faces have ornaments designed to use with the type.

The ornament should not be placed in the center between the two groups and should not be too large or too dark. If it is large and dark in tone, it will distract the reader's attention from the type (Fig. 8). The space between the two groups of type should be divided into eight parts and the ornament placed at the third division from the top (Fig. 9).

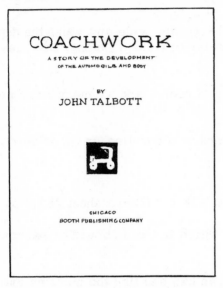

Fig. 8

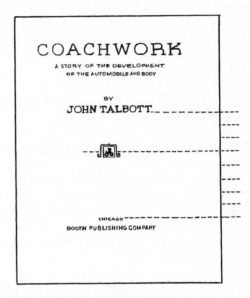

Fig. 9

THE LAYOUT

COPY (A)

SIZE: 6 in. by 9 in. deep

COPY: World Famous Books
A critical study
by Herbert Gay
Printers' Publishing Company
New York
1940

COPY (B)

COPY: Printer's Yearbook
by James M. Chase
Booth Publishing Company
New York, London, Paris

DIRECTIONS

1. Select either copy (A) or copy (B) and make a thumbnail sketch of the title page.

2. Have your sketch checked by the instructor.

3. After drawing the outside dimensions of the finished layout, plan the margins and draw the lines. Have the instructor check the margins before proceeding.

4. Complete the finished layout and mark it for the compositor.

SECTION I REVIEW

1. What is the difference between Roman type and Gothic type?

2. What part of a piece of type is the beard?

3. A customer wants a job printed on a sheet 4 in. wide and wants the depth to be well proportioned. Using either the Regular or Golden Oblong, find the depth of the sheet.

4. Make a small sketch showing an example of poor shape harmony and an example of good shape harmony.

5. Where on a sheet would you place one word or a one-line group of words?

6. What are the two types of balance?

7. How many pieces of paper 2 in. by 3 in. can be cut from a sheet 25 in. by 38 in.?

8. When placing a job on a single sheet, which margin should be narrowest and which widest?

9. Fold a sheet of paper 8 1/2 in. by 11 in. in half and find the margins that should be used in a book. The type page will be 24 picas wide.

10. What does a person mean when saying that the tone harmony on a job is poor?

11. Where is the focal point on a page and what is it used for?

12. Besides the squared shape, what other shapes are pleasing to use when grouping display lines?

13. What are the three parts of a book?

14. Name in order the parts of the preliminary section.

15. What kind of numbers are used for the folio in the preliminary section?

16. On what page in the preliminary section does the folio first appear?

17. On which page in the running head should the name of the book be placed?

18. What is the legend?

19. If the book half title consists of only one word or one line, where should it be placed on the page?

20. What pages in the preliminary section of a book use a sunken head?

Principles of Modern Layout

Unit 29   INTRODUCTION TO MODERN LAYOUT

Styles in typography change in the same manner as styles in dresses, shoes, hats or automobiles. During the last thirty years conditions changed the mode of living in this country and affected printed display so that a new style of typography was introduced. Airplanes, faster cars, radios, speedy trains and towering skyscrapers symbolize changing times and trends. People move quickly, eat rapidly and make quick decisions. Instead of taking time to read, they glance at printed matter. Therefore, it has become necessary for the layout man to arrange printing so that it can be read easily and quickly.

To meet these conditions, a new advertising force which is commonly known as the MODERN style has come into existence. It differs from conventional display in appearance only, for the old principles of design are applied in a new manner. Its main aims are novelty, effectiveness, simplicity and speedy reading.

This new style of typography was created in Germany and Austria by a small group of printers and designers who believed that they should use originality in designing instead of continuing to use the old conventional styles. In creating this new style, they applied some of the old traditional rules in a new way. Instead of using decorative types and borders, they adopted plain rule borders and plain Gothic or block types. At first, the experimenting typographers were unsuccessful, as they arranged the type so that it was difficult to read. They quickly realized their mistakes and made the necessary corrections so that the printed designs were easily read, effective and simple.

This new method of arranging printing spread throughout the European countries and was studied by American designers. Gradually, the layout men in this country attempted to arrange printing in the modern manner. At first they made the same mistakes as the European designers, with the result that this style did not become popular in this country. Their mistakes were soon corrected, and this method of arranging printing has steadily been gaining popularity.

This new style of arrangement has been named MODERN LAYOUT. It is not the result of a discovery of new principles of design or composition, but the result of entirely new methods of applying the basic conventional principles that have been used for years. Balance, proportion, tone harmony, etc. are principles of composition that do not change. It is the new manner in which these principles are interpreted that makes the arrangements different or modern.

MENU

Fig. 1

In conventional layout one word is placed $\frac{3}{8}$ down the page. This is a rule that printers have used for a long time.

As an example, in conventional layout one word on a page is placed 3/8 down the page in the focal point (Fig. 1). In modern layout, to add motion and allow for easy reading, one word or a group of words may be placed off center near the top of the page or near the bottom (Figs. 2, 3, 4). This allows the eye to read the message quickly as it enters the page or leaves it.

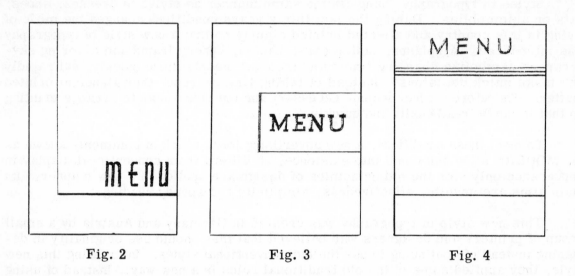

Fig. 2   Fig. 3   Fig. 4

In modern layout one word can be placed in any position on the page as long as it is easy to read.

THE LAYOUT		
COPY (A) Cover	COPY (B) Cover	COPY (C) Cover
SIZE: 6 in. by 9 in. deep	SIZE: 6 in. by 9 in. deep	SIZE: 6 in. by 9 in. deep
COPY: Announcing	COPY: Attention	COPY: Personal

DIRECTIONS

1. Select either copy (A), (B) or (C) and make at least two thumbnail sketches showing how you would arrange this cover in the modern manner.

2. You may use one color and black.

3. After the sketches are completed, show them to the instructor, marking the one you believe to be the best.

4. After having the sketch approved by the instructor, make the finished layout.

Unit 30   BASIC MODERN ARRANGEMENTS AND MODERN TYPE

The traditional method of positioning type masses on both sides of a center axis (Fig. 1) should be avoided in modern typography. A common method employed is that of arranging the type masses on either the left or right side of an imaginary vertical line which is placed to the left or right of the actual vertical center of the page (Fig. 2, 3, 4 and 5).

Fig. 1   Fig. 2   Fig. 3

The copy will regulate the position of this vertical. A short display line might be arranged to cause the vertical to be positioned as in Figs. 2 and 3, while a larger display head would cause it to be placed on the opposite side of the center as in Figs. 4 and 5. Notice that in both Fig. 3 and Fig. 5 each group of type is off center.

MODERN TYPE DESIGNS

In modern layout, only simple, easy-to-read type faces should be used. Modernism demands simplicity. Therefore, the type designs, as well as borders and ornaments, should be free from extravagant decoration.

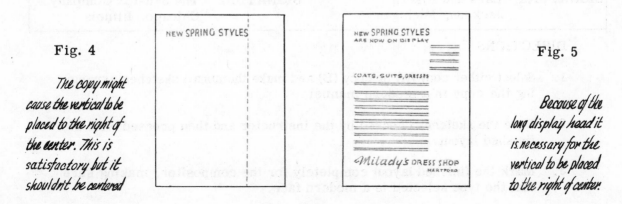

Fig. 4

The copy might cause the vertical to be placed to the right of the center. This is satisfactory but it shouldn't be centered

Fig. 5

Because of the long display head it is necessary for the vertical to be placed to the right of center.

As modern layouts give the reader the feeling of their being arranged in blocks, very straight and stiff, (Figs. 3 and 5), the type selected to use with such designs should be straight, stiff and simple. Therefore, Gothic types (Fig. 6) with strokes the same width and with no serifs are very appropriate. Types with curved serifs as the old style faces (Fig. 7) should not be employed, but block types with square serifs (Fig. 8) or Roman type with straight serifs (Fig. 9) may be used appropriately. The modern Roman faces (Fig. 9) with straight serifs are employed advantageously for the body or text, as they are easier to read in the small sizes than Gothics or block faces.

To give contrast to modern arrangements, script and cursive types (Fig. 10) are employed. Instead of being stiff and straight, they are free and graceful. Therefore, they would make an ideal contrast if a word or two were to be accented. Only one or two words of these types should be employed in a modern arrangement.

ABCDEFGHIJ

Fig. 6

ABCDEFGHIJ

Fig. 7

ABCDEFGH

Fig. 8

ABCDEFGHIJK

Fig. 9

ABCDEFGHIJ
ABCDEFGHIJ

Fig. 10

THE LAYOUT

COPY (A)	COPY (B)
SIZE: 6 in. by 9 in. deep	SIZE: 6 in. by 9 in. deep
DISPLAY HEAD: A lasting Perfume	DISPLAY HEAD: Would madam have charm?
SUBHEAD: Lars' and Rikers' Soap	SUBHEAD: San-tox Preparations
TEXT: Copy would be written after layout is completed; therefore, any amount of space may be used for the text.	TEXT: Any amount of space may be used in the layout for the text, as it would be written later.
SIGNATURE: Lars and Rikers Jackson, Michigan	SIGNATURE: The San-tox Company Chicago, Illinois

---

DIRECTIONS

1. Select either copy (A) or copy (B) and make thumbnail sketches arranging the copy in a modern manner.

2. Have the sketches checked by the instructor and then proceed with the finished layout.

3. Mark the finished layout completely for the compositor, making sure that the type selected is a modern face.

Unit 31   MOVEMENT IN MODERN LAYOUT

In modern typography, rules are used to give the impression of motion and to direct the eye from one part of the layout to the other. Modern designers use a rule to direct the eye through a layout because they believe that a line or rule is a "dot" or "point" in motion. When artists draw speeding automobiles (Figs. 1 and 2) or any fast moving object, they make streaks with lines trailing after the object to give it the impression of speed. Therefore, if a line or rule makes a car appear to the eye to be moving, it should move or direct the eye through a printed page.

Fig. 1   Fig. 2

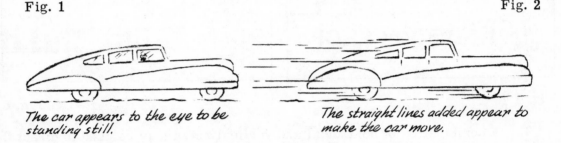

The car appears to the eye to be standing still.

The straight lines added appear to make the car move.

A few methods of using rules in modern printing design are listed below.

1.   Vertical (up and down) rules are used to direct the eye from one group of type to the other (Fig. 3) or to bring together type and illustrations (Fig. 4).

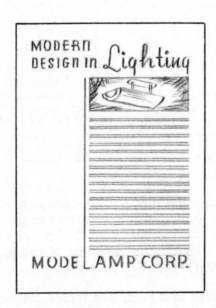

Fig. 3 *Note how the rule joins the group of type at the head of the page with that at the foot.*

Fig. 4 *The rule joins the head and cut to the signature in this arrangement.*

2. Horizontal rules, running across the page, are employed by the modern designer to make the eye travel across the page (Figs. 5 and 6).

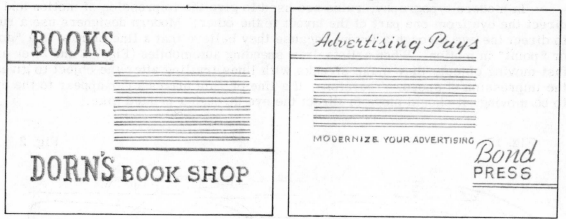

Fig. 5   Fig. 6

3. A combination of horizontal and vertical rules may be used to direct the eye across, down and out of the page (Fig. 7).

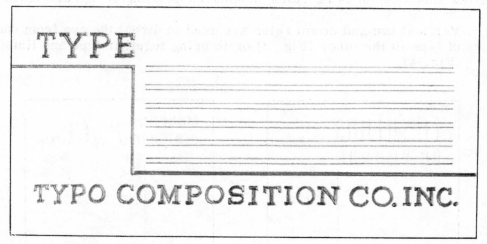

Fig. 7

In modern typography, the conventional use of margins is not employed. A margin is used around a sheet so that the type lines do not run to the edge of the paper, but unlike conventional layout, the rules bleed or run off the edge of the paper (Figs. 5, 6, 7). Besides the bleeding of rules, other units such as cuts and tint blocks are allowed to bleed.

Instead of a rule, any figure, object or cut that will lend itself to this structure can be substituted for rules as a means of introducing motion in a downward direction. For example, a cut of a slender product such as a pen or pencil might be employed instead of a rule. This cut (Fig. 8) will direct the eye through the advertisement just as the rule does.

84

RAIN *April Showers*

UMBRELLAS

RAINCOATS
RUBBERS

ADAMS & BROWN, INC.
THE STORE OF QUALITY

Fig. 8

THE LAYOUT

COPY (A)

SIZE: 6 in. by 9 in. deep

DISPLAY HEAD: The new styles

SUBHEAD: White for summer

TEXT: Copy will be written after the layout has been made so no definite amount of space has to be saved for the text.

SIGNATURE: Now at the Horn Boot Shop
Sixth Avenue, New York

COPY (B)

SIZE: 6 in. by 9 in. deep

DISPLAY HEAD: Venus, the better pencil

CUT: A pencil (any size you wish to use)

SUBHEAD: Tailored Writing

TEXT: Any amount of space desired may be used for the text, as the copy will be written after the layout has been completed.

SIGNATURE: Venus Pencil Company

DIRECTIONS

1. Select either copy (A) or copy (B) and make at least two thumbnail sketches, making sure a rule or some other unit will move the eye through the modern advertisement.

2. Have the sketches checked by the instructor.

3. After the sketches have been checked, proceed with the finished layout.

Unit 32   MODERN TYPE GROUPS

In conventional layout, type groups are usually arranged in a squared shape (Fig. 1), inverted pyramid (Fig. 2), dropline (Fig. 3) or the long and short line arrangement (Fig. 4).

THE ART OF
LETTERPRESS
ON DISPLAY
Fig. 1

THE BEST BUY
IS HERE
TODAY
Fig. 2

THE ART OF
LETTERPRESS
ON DISPLAY
Fig. 3

For old-time Chocolate flavor
the CHOC. brand
cannot be excelled
in any way
Fig. 4

In modern, it is satisfactory to group display type in the squared shape (Fig. 1) and the dropline shape (Fig. 3), but it should not be displayed in the long and short line arrangement (Fig. 4) or the inverted pyramid (Fig. 2). Instead of using the long and short line arrangement and the inverted pyramid, the lines should be grouped so that they are flush on either the left or right side of the group (Figs. 5 and 6).

Fig. 5   THE BEST BUY
IS HERE
TODAY

For old-time Chocolate flavor
the CHOC brand
cannot be excelled
in any way   Fig. 6

Conventional Grouping of type

Grouped flush to the left

Fig. 7

Conventional Grouping of type

Grouped flush to the right

Fig. 8

THE MODERN WAY TO DRESS FOR SPRING — SUITS TOPCOATS DRESSES — RICHARDS CLOTHES

THE MODERN WAY TO DRESS FOR SPRING — SUITS TOPCOATS DRESSES — RICHARD'S CLOTHES

A designer might arrange a page of type in the modern manner (Fig. 7) but use a conventional style of type grouping. Instead of being arranged so that the type group is made up of long and short lines, the type should line up on either the left or right side. All type groups in modern arrangements should line up on the imaginary vertical line (A-B, Fig. 8). If the group is to be placed to the right of the vertical, it should be squared on the left side and lined up on the vertical (Fig. 8). The group placed on the left of the vertical would line up on the vertical by having the right side of it square (Fig. 8).

Whenever it is possible, type groups should be squared in modern. If it is impossible to square the type, it should be set flush on either the left or right side of the imaginary vertical line.

THE LAYOUT

COPY (A)

SIZE: 11 in. by 8 1/2 in. deep

DISPLAY HEAD: Blue Moon Perfume

SUBHEAD: As smart as a whip

TEXT: No definite amount of space has to be reserved for the text, as the copy would be written after the layout has been finished.

LIST OF ITEMS: Lipstick, Face Powder, Bath Salts

CUT: 1 3/4 in. by 3 1/4 in. deep

SIGNATURE: Alice Luston Company

COPY (B)

SIZE: 8 1/2 in. by 11 in. deep

DISPLAY HEAD: January Cruises

SUBHEAD: Havana, Nassau, Bermuda

SUBHEAD: Eight days $185.00

TEXT: Use as much space as you desire for the text. The copy would be written after the layout has been completed.

SIGNATURE: The Southern Lines, Inc.

DIRECTIONS

1. Select either copy (A) or copy (B) and make at least two small thumb-nail sketches.

2. One color and black may be used.

3. Have the instructor check the sketches and then make the finished layout.

4. Mark the layout completely for the compositor.

Unit 33   ORNAMENTATION IN MODERN

When designing a modern layout where a little ornamentation is desired, it should be known that decorative borders and ornaments cannot be appropriately used. The types used in modern arrangements are plain, simple, without serifs or with square block serifs. So, in order to have borders and ornaments harmonize with the type, they should be simple in design. The type of decoration usually employed in modern consists of designs that are geometric in shape, such as squares, circles, triangles, stars, etc. These geometric spots can be used advantageously in modern arrangements, but should not be used without a purpose. If an open space in a layout has a geometric design to help fill the space, the ornament is wasted, as it will draw the eye away from the type (Fig. 1). Therefore, such designs should be used to attract the eye to the type so as to make the printing easy to read (Fig. 2).

Fig.1 *The triangular shaped ornament draws the readers attention away from the type message instead of aiding readability.*

Fig.2 *The ornament attracts the eye to the type and is a part of the display head.*

Another method of decorating modern arrangements is the use of bands or blocks of color, or blocks of black (Fig. 3). These are commonly called tint blocks by designers. It is customary to bleed these tint blocks, as the bleeding of cuts, rules, etc. is common practice among designers. At times, the layout man will use a gradation of rules instead of a tint block. A gradation of rules is an arrangement of rules starting from a thick one and grading their widths down to a thin one (Fig. 4). When using this method, the heaviest rule should always be on the outside away from the type to direct the eye into the advertisement (Fig. 5). If the heavy rule is nearest the type, it will lead the reader's eye out of the page (Fig. 6).

Fig. 3

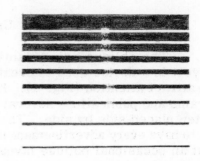

Fig. 4

Fig. 5

Fig. 6

THE LAYOUT

COPY (A)	COPY (B)
SIZE: 9 in. by 7 in. deep	SIZE: 7 in. by 9 in. deep
DISPLAY HEAD: Go to Europe by plane	DISPLAY HEAD: Florida, the land of sunshine
CUT: 3 in. by 2 in. deep	CUT: 2 in. by 3 in. deep
TEXT: No definite amount of space must be saved for the text	SUBHEAD: No winter in this resort
SIGNATURE: Atlanco Airways, Inc.	TEXT: No definite space to be saved for text
	SIGNATURE: Southern Steamship Lines

DIRECTIONS

1. Select either copy (A) or copy (B) and make two thumbnail sketches.

2. One color and black may be used.

3. After the sketches have been approved by the instructor, make the finished layout.

Unit 34   OBLIQUE AXIS

The oblique axis (slanting line) in modern layout is a device used to create added motion and to attract attention (Fig. 1). In newspapers, programs and publications several advertisements are often placed side by side. The usual arrangement is to have every advertisement in an upright position but an occasional oblique layout among the advertisements will attract attention.

Fig. 1

Fig. 2

When this type of arrangement is used, the design should be interesting so that the reader will not be conscious of the oblique arrangement of the layout. The type masses should be arranged on each side of the vertical as in other modern designs, and then placed on a slant. As we read from left to right, it is best to slant the copy in the same direction (Fig. 1), although very pleasing arrangements have been made by slanting the copy from right to left. When tilted at too great an angle, it forces the reader to turn his head or the sheet in order to read the message (Fig. 3). Therefore, the slant should not be great enough to impose difficulty in reading it.

Another method of unusual arrangement of layouts to attract attention is that employed in Fig. 4. This method is especially appropriate when the designer wishes to give the reader an impression of speed.

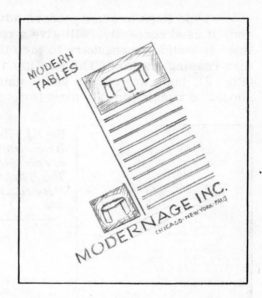

Fig. 3

THE LAYOUT

COPY (A)

SIZE: 7 in. by 10 in. deep

DISPLAY HEAD: Exhibition of Modern Cosmetics

TEXT: No definite amount of space has to be left for the text

SUBHEAD: First showing America

SIGNATURE: May Luton Salon

COPY (B)

SIZE: 7 in. by 10 in. deep

DISPLAY HEAD: The Individual in Evening Styles

CUT: 2 in. by 4 in. deep

CUT: 2 in. by 1 1/2 in. deep

TEXT: No definite amount of space has to be left for the text

SIGNATURE: J. J. Slater

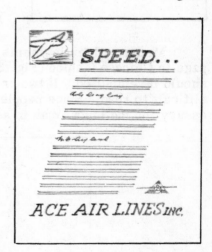

Fig. 4

DIRECTIONS

1. Make several thumbnail sketches of either copy (A) or copy (B), arranging the layout, using the oblique axis, and one color and black.

2. Select the arrangement you consider to be the better one and have it checked by the instructor.

3. Make the finished layout.

Unit 35 · DISTORTED TYPE LINES

Designers of printing at times distort type lines in order to give a page a modern appearance. If handled correctly, pleasing arrangements can be created by using this method.

Type lines in some modern advertisements run up and down the page (Fig. 1), and, if used correctly, will give a page a modern appearance. In order to read this line, it would be necessary to turn the sheet so that the line acts more like a border than reading matter. The line used in this manner should not be an important one (Fig. 2), but a line of copy that is unimportant (Fig. 1). Only a single line or sentence should be running in this direction, not two or three lines.

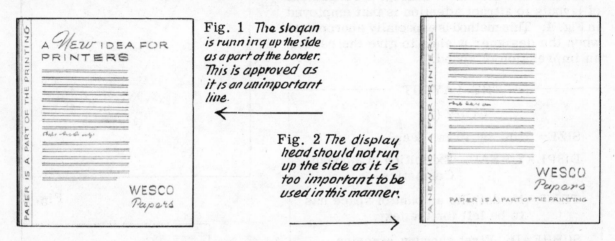

Fig. 1 *The slogan is running up the side as a part of the border. This is approved as it is an unimportant line.*

Fig. 2 *The display head should not run up the side as it is too important to be used in this manner.*

Modern advertisements are also arranged with type running up and down the page in Chinese fashion (Fig. 3). When the designer uses this method, only one word should be employed. If two or three words (Fig. 4), are set in this manner, they are difficult to read. Since people are not accustomed to reading up and down, it is necessary for the layout man to select an unimportant word.

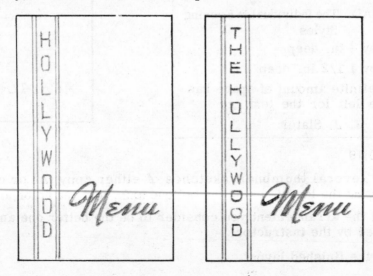

Fig. 3   Fig. 4

Type lines in some advertisement are arranged to turn corners. This style is usually employed when it is possible for the type to be used as a part of a border design (Fig. 5). An important line should never be arranged in this manner, as it is difficult to read.

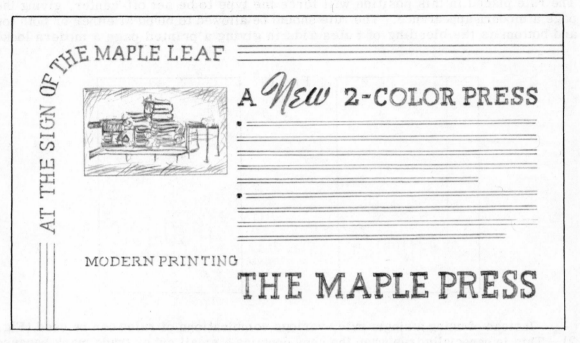

Fig. 5

┌─────────────── THE LAYOUT ───────────────┐

COPY

SIZE: 7 in. by 10 in. deep

DISPLAY HEAD: Style and Low Price

TEXT: No definite amount of space has to be saved for the copy.

CUT: 2 in. by 4 in. deep

SIGNATURE: Campbell Brothers
Lexington Avenue, New York

└───┘

DIRECTIONS

1. Make several thumbnail sketches of the copy, arranging it in a modern manner. One color and black may be used.

2. Have the sketches checked by the instructor.

3. Make the finished layout.

4. Completely mark the copy for the instructor.

Unit 36   LEFT HAND VERTICAL RULE

When designing a page containing a small amount of copy for which a modern arrangement is desired, a rule down the left side of the page may be used (Fig. 1). The rule placed in this position will force the type to be set off-center, giving the page a modern appearance. The rule should be allowed to bleed at either or both top and bottom as the bleeding of rules aids in giving a printed page a modern look.

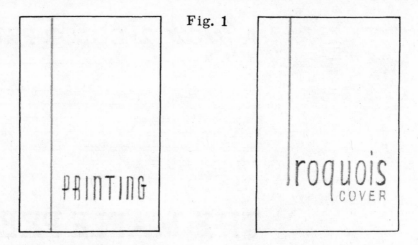

Fig. 1

Instead of using a single rule, various combinations of rules can be used (Fig. 2). This is especially true when the copy contains a small cut or trade mark because the rules and cut may be combined into a simple border arrangement.

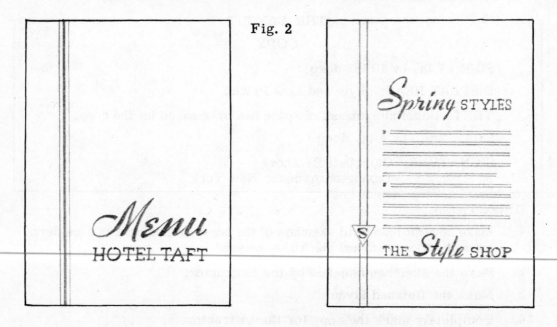

Fig. 2

Besides using the rule down the left side, a change in design can be secured by combining horizontal rules with vertical rules if the copy permits. Various arrangements can be formed by combining the rules in this manner (Figs. 3, 4 and 5).

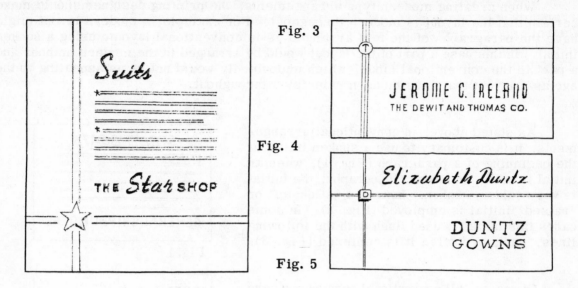

Fig. 3

Fig. 4

Fig. 5

THE LAYOUT

COPY (A)

SIZE: 4 in. by 6 in. deep

DISPLAY HEAD: Announcing Grand Opening

CUT: Small circular trade mark

TEXT: No definite amount of space is to be left for the text.

SIGNATURE: Hotel Watson

COPY (B)

SIZE: 4 in. by 6 in. deep

DISPLAY HEAD: Introducing Original Designs

TEXT: No definite amount of space is to be left for the text.

SIGNATURE: Alpha Press

DIRECTIONS

1. Select either copy (A) or copy (B) and make several thumbnail sketches.

2. One color and black may be used.

3. Show the thumbnail sketches to the instructor.

4. Make the finished layout, marking it for the compositor.

Unit 37   PARAGRAPH TREATMENT AND THE
USE OF THE TYPOGRAPHIC DOT

When creating modern type arrangements, the printing designer should make certain that the layout is modern throughout. For example, a modern layout might have the paragraphs of the text arranged as in conventional layout, using a sunken initial. In this case a part of the layout would be arranged in the modern manner and a part in the conventional mode, which undoubtedly would not be as appealing to the eye as a layout that uses modern principles throughout.

As stated above, in conventional arrangements, it is customary to use a sunken initial at the beginning of a paragraph (Fig. 1), when an initial is used. In modern typography, the initial is very seldom sunken. Instead a "stick-up" or "raised" initial is employed (Fig. 2). In some cases this initial is used flush with the following lines, but more often it is centered (Fig. 3).

Of course, all conventional paragraphs are not started with an initial. Some are indented (Fig. 4). In modern, an indented paragraph is not used. Instead the first line is set flush with the others (Fig. 5).

It is also customary to use a typographic dot or a star at the beginning of the paragraph (Fig. 6).

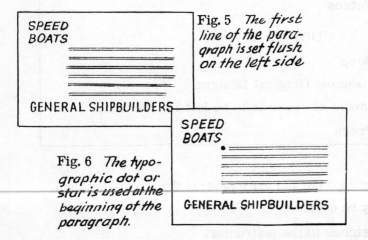

Fig. 1

Fig. 2

Fig. 3

Fig. 4

Fig. 5 *The first line of the paragraph is set flush on the left side*

Fig. 6 *The typographic dot or star is used at the beginning of the paragraph.*

The typographic dot or star is also used in modern to separate words in place of the comma (Fig. 7) and in place of a rule to lead the eye (Fig. 8). It should be remembered that the type should always stand out more than the dots or stars whenever they are employed, as the type carries the printed message.

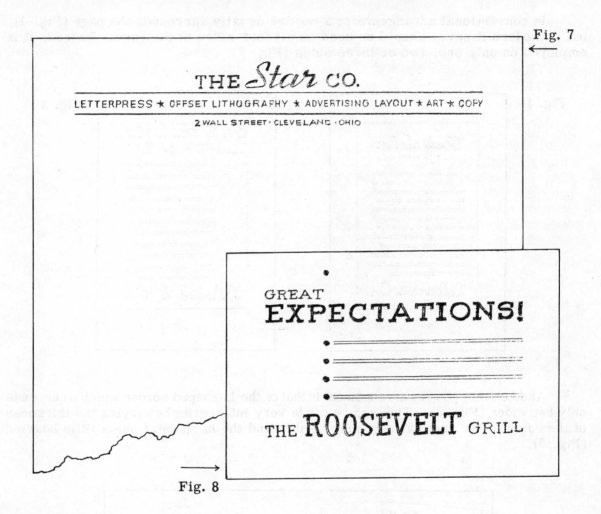

Fig. 7

Fig. 8

THE LAYOUT

DIRECTIONS

1. Make several thumbnail sketches of a modern business or name card for yourself, using your own copy.

2. One color and black may be used.

3. After sketches have been made, have them checked by the instructor.

4. Make the finished layout 3 1/2 in. by 2 in. deep.

Unit 38   MODERN RULE BORDERS

As already explained, rules are used in modern to give motion to the layout. They also are used as borders.

In conventional arrangements a border usually surrounds the page (Fig. 1), but in modern it never should be used on all four sides of the page. Instead, it is employed on only one, two or three sides (Fig. 2).

Fig. 1
Fig. 2

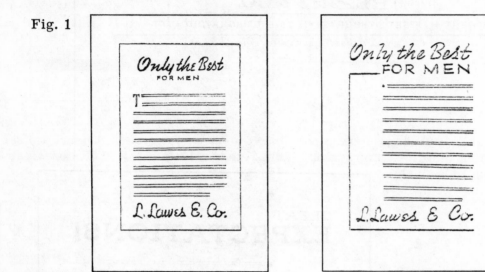

Another very popular arrangement is that of the L-shaped border which surrounds only two sides (Fig. 3). This can be made very interesting by varying the thickness of the rules. The vertical rule may be thin and the horizontal one a little heavier (Fig. 3).

Fig. 3

Rules forming boxes that bleed on one side are also employed in various ways. This method is especially popular in arranging modern cover designs (Fig. 4). By having two sides of the box in a heavy rule, a shadow effect can also be secured (Fig. 5).

Fig. 4

Fig. 5

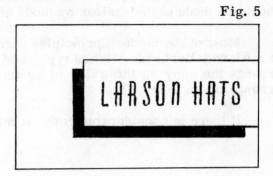

Innumerable arrangements are possible by using rule borders. Hence we see that by combining them with tint blocks, cuts, etc., a large variety of modern arrangements can be secured.

LAYOUT TEST

COPY (A)	COPY (B)
SIZE: 6 in. by 8 in. deep	SIZE: 4 in. by 9 in. deep
DISPLAY HEAD: Are You Straining your Eyes?	DISPLAY HEAD: To Gentlemen who desire the Best
CUT: 4 in. by 3 in. deep	CUT: 1 1/2 in. by 2 in. deep
TWO CIRCULAR CUTS: Each 1 1/2 in. in diameter	TEXT: No definite amount of space has to be reserved for the text
TEXT: No definite amount of space has to be reserved for the text	SIGNATURE: N. Mullins and Co. The Man's Store
SIGNATURE: Whitcomb Optical Co.	

DIRECTIONS FOR THE TEST

1. Make thumbnail sketches of either copy (A) or copy (B) arranging the copy in the modern manner.

2. One color and black may be used.

3. Select the sketch you believe to be the better one.

4. Do not show your selection to the instructor, but proceed with the finished layout.

5. Mark finished layout for compositor and have the instructor check it.

Unit 39   BASIC MODERN LETTERHEAD ARRANGEMENTS

Business concerns at times wish to have their letterheads re-designed and modernized. As the arranging of letterheads differs from other types of layout work because of the large space that has to be reserved for the written letter, a study should be made of the various methods of designing letterheads in the modern mode.

Most of the modern principles already studied can be applied in the designing of modern letterheads. When type, and type alone, is to be used, it is possible to arrange the copy on the sides of an imaginary vertical line, as in other modern arrangements (Fig. 1).

If there is considerable copy, it may be counter balanced (Fig. 2).

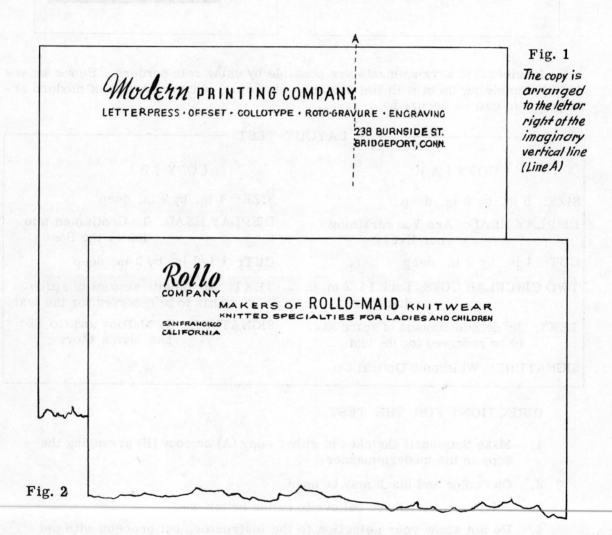

Fig. 1

The copy is arranged to the left or right of the imaginary vertical line (Line A)

Fig. 2

As in other modern layouts, rules are employed to add motion and decoration. Therefore, a rule may be used in various ways, either in black or color (Figs. 3 and 4).

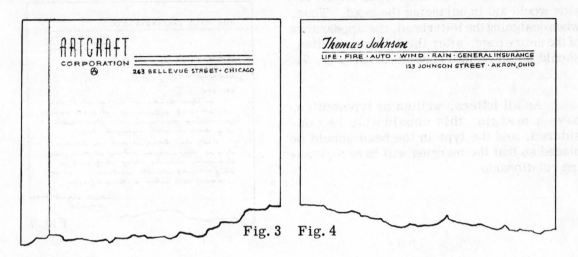

Fig. 3   Fig. 4

In some cases, a letterhead must be formal, yet modern. This type of letterhead can be created by centering the type, and modernizing it by allowing the rules to bleed (Fig. 5).

Tint blocks and bands of color, or black, also aid in forming modern letterheads. They may be used in various ways, but never should be so dark and so large as to draw attention from the type (Fig. 6).

Fig. 5   Fig. 6

As the type is placed off center on practically all modern arrangements, it should be known that the weight, or the largest group of type, would be most effective if placed on the right side of the letterhead because the salutation when typed on the left side would aid in balancing the head. Thus, when designing the letterhead, the appearance of the entire page, after the letter is written, should be taken into consideration (Fig. 7).

As all letters, written or typewritten, have a margin, this should also be considered, and the type in the head should be placed so that the margins will have a pleasing relationship.

Fig. 7

THE LAYOUT

COPY (A) LETTERHEAD

SIZE: 8 1/2 in. by 11 in. deep

COPY: The Ainsworth Company
Leather and Rubber Footwear
122 Huron Street
Chicago, Illinois

COPY (B) LETTERHEAD

SIZE: 8 1/2 in. by 11 in. deep

COPY: The Johnson Coal Co.
Anthracite and Bituminous Coal and Coke
Toledo, Ohio

DIRECTIONS

1. Make at least three thumbnail sketches of either copy (A) or copy (B).

2. One color and black may be used.

3. Have the thumbnail sketches checked by the instructor.

4. Make the finished layout.

Unit 40   PLACING TRADEMARK ON MODERN LETTERHEADS

Sometimes a letterhead may seem to be lacking individuality when designed with type only. The design may be improved by the addition of a trademark or a modern ornament. Also, since the introduction of modern arrangements, many old letterheads containing trademarks have been redesigned by applying the principles of modern typography.

When using a trademark, the same principles of modern arrangement are employed as on other letterheads. The trademark may be placed either to the left or right of the center (Figs. 1 and 2).

Fig. 1   Fig. 2

If a formal yet modern appearance is desired, the trademark may be centered, used without a rule, or may break the rule in the center (Fig. 3). At times, the cut can be appropriately placed above or below the rule (Fig. 4).

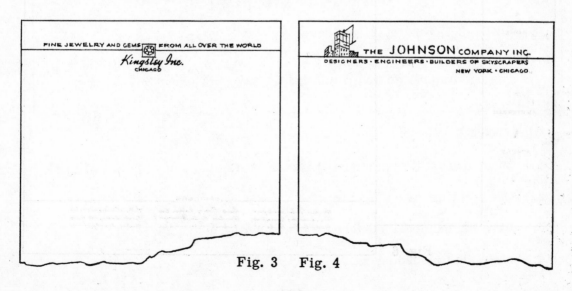

Fig. 3   Fig. 4

There are, of course, innumerable methods besides those suggested of placing the cut. At times, the copy will suggest an arrangement, and in practically every case the positioning of the rule and trademark will depend upon the copy and should be arranged according to the copy. For example, the copy might contain, besides the name and address of a company, a long list of officers or products. In order to place them at the top of the letterhead, so much space might be used that there would not be enough blank paper left for the typewritten letter. Therefore, the list of officers might be placed in the left margin, or at the foot of the page (Figs. 5 and 6).

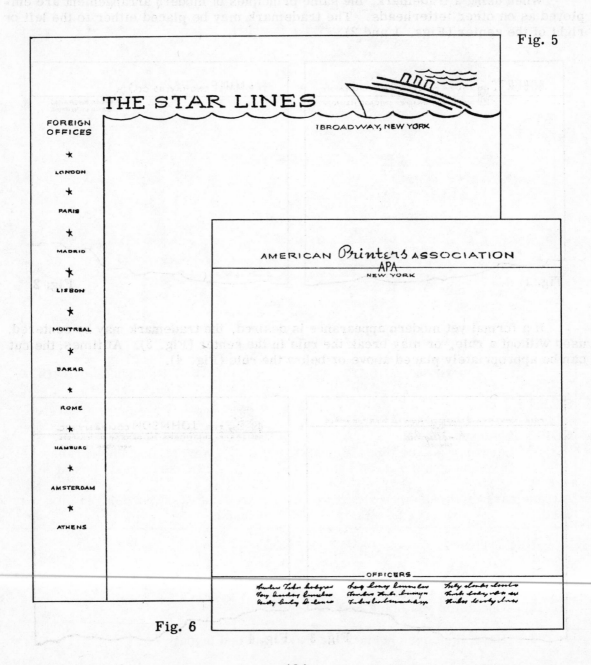

Fig. 5

Fig. 6

At times, instead of the trademark the picture of the product is used on a company's letterhead. They might desire to have the product placed so that every reader of the letter would certainly see the cut. Therefore, it is necessary to know the location of the focal point on a letterhead.

As we all know, the eyes of every reader of a letter move to the salutation first. Therefore, that is the focal point of the letter. If the cut of the product were placed as close to this focal point as possible, undoubtedly every reader would see it before reading the letter (Fig. 7).

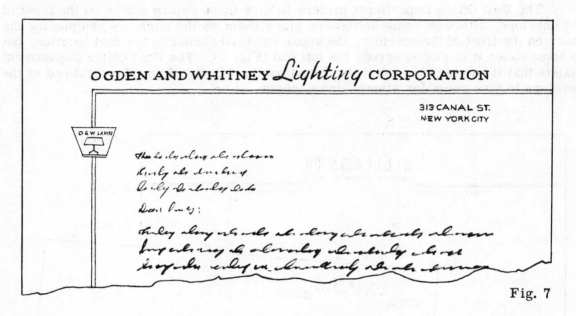

OGDEN AND WHITNEY *Lighting* CORPORATION

313 CANAL ST.
NEW YORK CITY

Fig. 7

THE LAYOUT

COPY (A) LETTERHEAD	COPY (B) LETTERHEAD
SIZE: 8 1/2 in. by 11 in. deep	SIZE: 8 1/2 in. by 11 in. deep
COPY: Potomac Co., Inc. Lumber, Ties and Mine Materials 16 Washington Street, Scranton, Pa.	COPY: Mirsen Studio Advertising Photography 12 Court Street, Los Angeles
A trademark of any desired size may be used.	A trademark of any desired size may be used.

DIRECTIONS

1. Make thumbnail sketches of either copy (A) or copy (B).

2. One color and black may be used.

3. Have sketches checked and make finished layout.

Unit 41   CONTINUITY IN THE DESIGN OF BUSINESS FORMS

Many business concerns desire to have their letterheads, envelope corners, billheads and other business forms arranged so that they are similar in design (Fig. 1). When this is desired, the layout man has to arrange a letterhead design that can be used throughout. The copy on the envelop may be slightly different, but should be the same in design. The return mark on the envelope usually gives the firm name and address so that the letter can be returned if necessary.

The Post Office Department prefers to have these return marks on the front of the envelope, although some designers place them on the back. When placing the mark on the front of the envelope, the upper left hand corner is the best location, but in some cases it is placed across the left end (Fig. 2). The Post Office Department insists that it be placed at least three and one half inches from the right end of the envelope to give room for stamps and cachets.

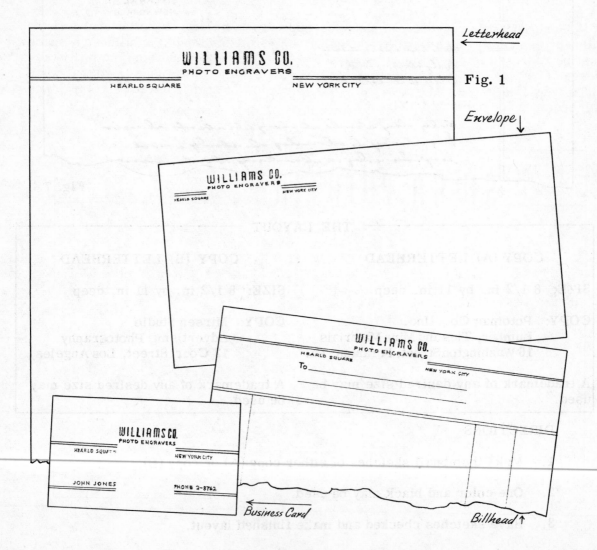

Letterhead ←

Fig. 1

Envelope ↓

Business Card

Billhead ↑

It is usually best when designing the envelope to sketch in the stamp and write the address on the dummy so that a picture of the complete envelope can be studied (Fig. 2).

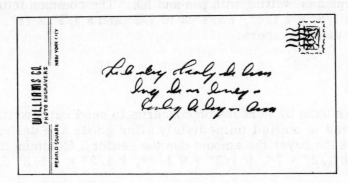

Fig. 2

Generally it is very easy to place the same design on both the letterhead and the billhead, especially when they are the same width. At the top of the billhead a space must be reserved to place the name and address of the person to whom the bill is addressed (Fig. 3). This, in most cases, is placed to the left of center so that when folded it will be in the right position to use in window or transo envelopes (envelopes with openings for name and address).

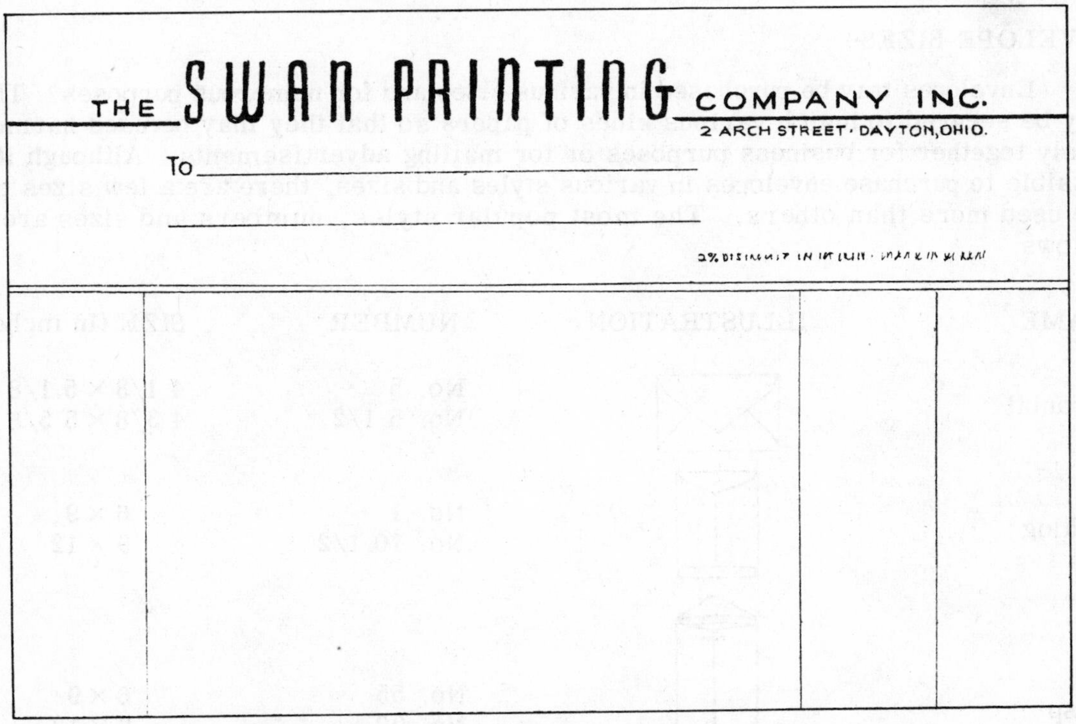

THE **SWAN PRINTING** COMPANY INC.

2 ARCH STREET · DAYTON, OHIO.

To_____

_____

Fig. 3

PRINTING LAYOUT AND DESIGN

STANDARD LETTERHEAD SIZES

Business letterheads, billheads and statements are usually printed on a paper called bond. This paper is made with a relatively hard finish which forms an excellent surface for typing or writing with pen and ink. The common letterhead sizes are 8 1/2" × 5 1/2", 8 1/2" × 7 1/4", 7 1/4" × 10 1/2" and 8 1/2" × 11". The last named size is used more than the others.

BILLHEAD SIZES

Billheads are used by persons or concerns to send out a written charge to the buyer. The billhead is mailed immediately after goods are delivered or services rendered and gives the buyer the amount due the sender. Common billhead sizes are 8 1/2" × 4 2/3", 8 1/2" × 7", 8 1/2" × 9 1/3", 8 1/2" × 5 1/2" and 8 1/2" × 14".

STATEMENT SIZES

The statement is sent out once a month to inform the buyer of the amount due the sender. The word statement usually appears at the top of the sheet. Common statement sizes are 8 1/2" × 5 1/2", 5 2/3" × 11", 5 1/2" × 5 1/2", 4 1/8" × 5 1/2", 3 1/2" × 8 1/2" and 5 1/2" × 6". Billheads and statements may be purchased cut to size and pen ruled with both vertical and horizontal lines. A blank space is left at the top for printing the copy.

ENVELOPE SIZES

Envelopes may be purchased in various sizes and for numerous purposes. They may be secured to match various kinds of papers so that they may be used harmoniously together for business purposes or for mailing advertisements. Although it is possible to purchase envelopes in various styles and sizes, there are a few sizes that are used more than others. The most popular styles, numbers and sizes are as follows:

NAME	ILLUSTRATION	NUMBER	SIZE (In inches)
Baronial		No. 5	4 1/8 × 5 1/8
		No. 5 1/2	4 3/8 × 5 5/8
Catalog		No. 1	6 × 9
		No. 10 1/2	9 × 12
Clasp		No. 55	6 × 9
		No. 90	9 × 12

NAME	ILLUSTRATION	NUMBER	SIZE (In inches)
Commercial		No. 6 3/4	3 5/8 × 6 1/2
		No. 6	3 3/8 × 6
Monarch		No. 7 3/4	3 7/8 × 7 1/2
Official		No. 10	4 1/8 × 9 1/2
Postage Saver		No. 6 3/4	3 5/8 × 6 1/2
		No. 10	4 1/8 × 9 1/2
Window (One Piece)		No. 6 3/4	3 5/8 × 6 1/2
		No. 10	4 1/8 × 9 1/2
Window		No. 6 3/4	3 5/8 × 6 1/2
		No. 10	4 1/8 × 9 1/2

THE LAYOUT

COPY (A)

LETTERHEAD SIZE: 8 1/2 in. by 11 in. deep

ENVELOPE SIZE: 7 1/2 in. by 3 7/8 in. deep

BILLHEAD SIZE: 8 1/2 in. by 5 1/2 in. deep

COPY: Atlantic Cleaning Company
623 Ocean Avenue, New York City

COPY (B)

LETTERHEAD SIZE: 8 1/2 in. by 11 in. deep

ENVELOPE SIZE: 7 1/2 in. by 3 7/8 in. deep

BILLHEAD SIZE: 8 1/2 in. by 5 1/2 in. deep

COPY: Crocker Coal Company
123 Main Street, Albany, New York

DIRECTIONS

1. Select either copy (A) or (B) and make at least two thumbnail sketches of a letterhead, envelope and billhead, using the same design on each.

2. One color and black may be used.

3. Have the instructor check the thumbnail sketches.

4. Make the finished layouts of the letterhead, envelope and billhead.

SECTION II REVIEW

1. For what purposes are rules used in modern layouts?

2. Find at least two things that are incorrect in the modern arrangement in Fig. 1.

3. Why should rules and cuts bleed in modern arrangements?

4. What types of decoration are employed in modern layout?

5. What is wrong with the arrangement of the modern cover in Fig. 2?

Fig. 1

6. Should the first letter of a paragraph in a modern layout be a "sunken initial" or a "stickup initial"?

7. When should a rule, used as a border, be placed on all four sides of the type page of a modern layout?

8. How much blank space does the Post Office Department require the printer to leave on the right side of the envelope for the address and the stamp?

9. Where would be the best location on a letterhead to place a cut of an article so that every reader would be certain to see it?

10. What is a window or transo envelope?

Fig. 2

Section III
Type

Unit 42   TYPEFOUNDING

The tool used more than any other by layout men is type. It is a part of every layout; therefore every layout man and typesetter should have a thorough knowledge of type and its use.

The making or casting of type is called typefounding. In early days the printer cast his own type, and it was more than a hundred years after the invention of printing before typefounding became a business in itself.

Type is made of an alloy of lead, tin, antimony and copper. The lead is a soft, cheap metal and used alone, could be easily crushed. Therefore, the other metals are used for the following reasons: antimony, to harden; tin, to toughen; and copper, to make it durable. The percentage of lead, tin, antimony and copper varies according to the size of type. For small sizes of type there is more antimony used and less lead than in 72-point and the larger sizes.

MAKING TYPE BY HAND

In the early days of typefounding the matrix, or mold, was made by hand. The printer designed his own letters of the alphabet, and from his designs he cut the letter into the matrix by hand and then cast his type.

After drawing the letter, the first step in making the matrix by hand was to make the counter punch. This was accomplished by drawing the letter on the end of a small bar of soft steel, cutting away the blank part of the letter and thus allowing the shape of the open parts of the letter or counter to be raised. Note the tracing of the letter "O" on the bar of steel in Fig. 1 and the cutting away of the open parts in Fig. 2.

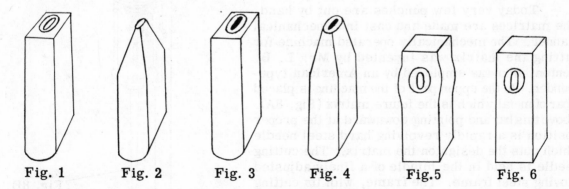

Fig. 1   Fig. 2   Fig. 3   Fig. 4   Fig.5   Fig. 6

When the counter was perfect it was hardened and used to make the counter-punch drive. This was done by taking another piece of soft steel and driving the counter punch into the end of it (Fig. 3).

The force of the drive gave a very rough and ragged outline of the letter around the sunken part. After tooling and finishing, this became the character from which the matrix was made. When this was perfect, the soft steel was hardened and the punch, Fig. 4, was ready to be stamped into the copper bar. This punch stamped into the copper produced the rough matrix (Fig. 5). This needed to be smoothed and the sides trued up before being placed into the hand mold (Fig. 6).

The matrix alone could not form the piece of type, but by placing it in a mold the type could be cast. Until 1838 types were cast from matrices in small hand molds. This was a slow method, as only about 400 letters an hour could be produced. The mold consisted of two parts fitting closely together, with the matrix containing the sunken image of the letter at one end, and an opening in the other through which to pour the metal (Fig. 7). The mold was held in the left hand while the right hand was used to pour the metal. The founder would then jerk the mold to bring the metal up into contact with the matrix and then would open the mold and throw out the type.

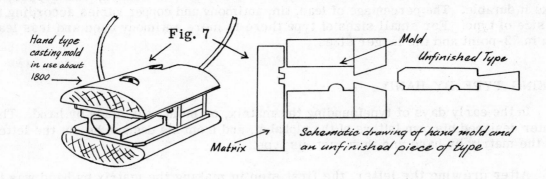

Fig. 7

Hand type casting mold in use about 1800

Matrix

Mold

Unfinished Type

Schematic drawing of hand mold and an unfinished piece of type

MAKING MATRICES AND CASTING TYPE BY MACHINE

Today very few punches are cut by hand. The matrices are made and cast in a mechanical manner. The mechanically operated machine for cutting the matrix was invented by Mr. L. B. Benton, who was employed by an American type-founder. In the upper part of the machine is placed a bar of metal which is the future matrix (Fig. 8A). Above this bar and pointing downward at the proper position is a rapidly revolving hard steel needle which cuts the design on the matrix. The cutting needle is held in the middle of a finely adjusted moving steel frame. The frame, with its cutting needle, is controlled in all its motions by a rod suspended below, which is moved over a diagram or pattern (Fig. 8B). All the motions of this rod over the diagram are duplicated by the needle on the matrix. Therefore any design that is drawn

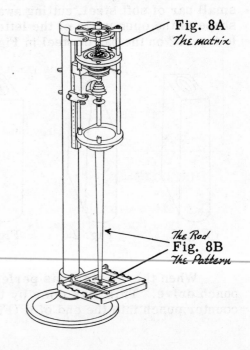

Fig. 8A
The matrix

The Rod
Fig. 8B
The Pattern

can be duplicated on the matrix. One pattern may be used for cutting matrices for several different sizes of the same letter simply by adjusting the machine to the size desired. Besides the hand and the mechanical methods there is also another method of making the matrices by an electrotype process.

In 1838 the Bruce typecasting machine was invented. This operated in the same manner as the hand mold, but in this machine the production was increased to about 100 a minute for ordinary sizes. The hot metal was pumped into the mold which automatically opened and discharged the type. Neither the hand mold nor the Bruce caster produced finished types. On the bottom of each type there was attached a wedge shaped jet. This had to be removed by hand, and the groove cut at the bottom to form the feet.

Near the end of the 19th century the Barth typecasting machine came into use and today produces complete finished types at the rate of more than 10,000 an hour, depending upon the size type being cast. In this machine the mold is non-opening, as in the Bruce machine. The type is cast and pushed out by a blade the exact size of the type body, which also cleans the mold as it pushes the type out. As the type leaves the mold, the jet is broken off, the bottom groove forming the feet is cut and the burrs on all corners are taken off by knife edges. On small types this machine can cast 250 a minute. One man can operate two machines and sometimes three.

THE LAYOUT

MAILING CARD

SIZE: 4 1/2 in. by 5 1/2 in. deep

DISPLAY HEAD: Perfection

TEXT: Newly styled suites of incomparable charm in arrangements of one to four rooms. Some with serving pantries. Yearly lease or shorter periods. Unfurnished if desired.

SIGNATURE: The Madison
15 E. 58th Street, New York

DIRECTIONS

1. Make two thumbnail sketches of the mailing card and select the one you consider to be the better.

2. One color and black may be used.

3. Have the instructor check your selection.

4. Make the finished layout.

Unit 43   INTRODUCTION TO TYPE

KINDS OF TYPE

The composing room of printing plants usually contains a large variety of type. These types when classified would come under one of the following divisions: Roman, Gothic, block, italic, text and script (Fig. 1).

Fig. 1

Words **People** **Traffic** *Rooms* 𝕸𝖆𝖐𝖊𝖘 *Ascent*

Roman   Gothic   Block   Italic   Text   Script

MODERN AND OLDSTYLE ROMAN

Roman types are of two kinds, oldstyle and modern. One difference between the oldstyle and the modern Roman is in the thickness of the stems and the hairlines. There is very little difference in the thickness of the lines in the oldstyle, whereas modern Roman types have a strong contrast between the thin and thick strokes (Fig. 2).

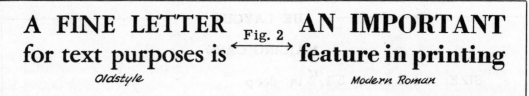

A FINE LETTER *Fig. 2* AN IMPORTANT
for text purposes is ⟵⟶ feature in printing
Oldstyle   Modern Roman

Serif formations in modern and oldstyle type faces differ decidedly. The serif at the top of the oldstyle tilts on some lower case letters as the r, n, l, p etc., while the serifs on the Roman are straight (Fig. 3). The serifs on the oldstyle types are formed by a line curving from the stroke of the letter. This line forms a bracket which gives the serif a curved appearance (Fig. 4). The serif on modern Roman types is very straight and angular. Where the serif meets the stroke of the type, it forms a sharp right angle instead of curving as in the oldstyle faces (Fig. 5).

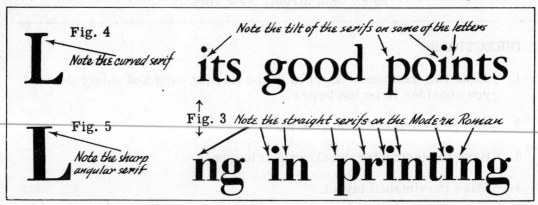

Fig. 4 *Note the curved serif* *Note the tilt of the serifs on some of the letters*

L its good points

Fig. 5 *Note the sharp angular serif* Fig. 3 *Note the straight serifs on the Modern Roman*

L ng in printing

The difference in the design of these two Roman types makes it unwise to use them in combination with each other. It is much safer to use types of either one classification or another throughout the entire advertisement. The oldstyle types should be used on rough surfaced antique papers while the modern Roman faces are appropriate for the smooth coated papers.

TYPE FONTS

Fig. 6 →

A font of type is an assortment of any one size and style (Fig. 6). The font includes lower-case (small letters), figures, caps (capital letters) and punctuation marks. Often the following reference marks are also included in the font:

Asterisk	*	Dagger	†
Double Dagger	‡	Section	§
Parallel	‖	Paragraph	¶

Some fonts also contain fractions, (¼ ½ ¾ ⅛ ⅜ ⅝), diphthongs, (Æ Œ æ œ Æ Œ æ œ), special characters, (% ‰ ¢ ℞ ℥ ☉ « » ℔), and ligatures, (fi fl ff ffi ffl).

```
A B C D E F G
H I J K L M N
O P Q R S T U
V W X Y Z & $
1 2 3 4 5 6 7 8 9 0
a b c d e f g h i j k
l m n o p q r s t u
v w x y z ff fi fl ffi ffl
. , - ' ' : ; ! ?
```

TYPE FAMILIES

Types that belong to one family are those that have the same general appearance, except that some faces may be either light, bold, italic, condensed or extended. The Goudy family consists of Goudy Oldstyle, Goudy Oldstyle Italic, Goudy Hand-tooled, Goudy Bold, Goudy Bold Italic, etc. (Fig. 7).

Fig. 7

ABCDEFGHJ abcdefgh 123

Goudy Handtooled

ABCDEFGHIJKLMNO & abcdefghijklmnopqrstu 789

Goudy Bold

ABCDEFGHIJKLMNOP& abcdefghijklmnopqrstuvwxyzabcdef 456

Goudy Text

ABCDEFGHIJKLMNOP& abcdefghijklmnopqrstuv 456

Goudy Bold Italic

Goudy Swash

ABCDEFGHIJK LMNOPQRSTUV a e m n t k v w ct

TYPE SERIES

Type is made by the type-founders in a graded series from 6-point to 72-point (Fig. 8). The sizes commonly made are 6-, 8-, 10-, 12-, 14-, 18-point, and then in the multiples of 6-points to 48-point. Above 48-point 60-, 72-, 84-, 96-, and occasionally as large as 144-point are made. In some cases type is made as small as 3-point.

WOOD TYPE

When large sizes of type are used to print signs and posters, wood type is usually employed. The size of wood type is designated by line instead of point, a line being equal to one pica. The smallest stock size of wood type is a 3-line letter which is the same size as 36-point type. Wood type can be secured in the following sizes: 3-line, 4-, 5-, 6-, 7-, 8-, 10-, 15-, 20-, 25-, 30-, 35-, 40-, 50-, 60-, 75-, 100- and 125- line. Larger sizes are usually known as half-sheet letters, 21 inches; one-sheet letters, 42 inches; two-sheet letters, 84 inches, etc. Wood type has no shoulder at the sides, bottom or top of the letter and, thus, requires letterspacing and linespacing.

THE LAYOUT

COPY COVER

SIZE: 6 in. by 9 in. deep

COPY: Distinguished Packard

CUT: A cut or trademark of any desired size may be used.

DIRECTIONS

1. Make at least two thumbnail sketches of the cover.

2. One color and black may be used.

3. Have the instructor check the sketches.

4. Make the finished layout.

6-POINT
for the present existence of the Trade Composition House, and this development will prove of great advantage to the industry in

8-POINT
who devotes his time to one task naturally becomes most efficient. This evolution in the print-

10-POINT
THE TREND OF ALL INDUSTRY

12-POINT
TREND OF ALL INDUSTRY

14-POINT
THE EYES OF CHILDREN
PIERCE THE VEIL OF MYSTERY

18-POINT
A NOBLER SERVICE
CANNOT BE DONE THAN

24-POINT
FROM BEYOND

30-POINT
NEW IDEAS

36-POINT
ANY PORT

42-POINT
RESEARCH

48-POINT
Admirable

60-POINT
Has All

72-POINT
People

Fig. 8

Unit 44   USE OF TYPE

Type is used in printing to carry a message from one company or person to several hundred companies or thousands of persons. This message should be arranged to attract attention, appear pleasing to the eye and, above all, to be easily read.

In arranging a printed message, the compositor should give considerable thought to the selection of type. Designers and printers have various type designs to use and, in many cases, enough to be confusing.

It is not unusual to see a piece of printing on which four or five families of type have been used (Fig. 1). Printing employing many different type faces is difficult to read because the variety of type designs attracts too much of the reader's attention. The reader becomes more interested in the different types than in the message. If only one type design is employed, the reader will be more likely to read the message without noticing the type (Fig. 2).

The layout man will do well not to increase his task by attempting to use several styles of type on a page while endeavoring to give a design unity and style of its own. To use several styles is to multiply the difficulties in the way of effective display.

By using only one family of type on a job, the designer is not greatly restricted. With a single font of type he has the caps and lower case of the Roman, as well as the caps and lower case of the italic, besides various sizes of each.

Thus it is possible to secure variety in the layout by using one family of type. In order to make a printed page interesting, it is not necessary to change the face, since a contrast can be secured on a page by using one family.

JACQUILINE
Importer, Exporter
Rare Antiques
Oriental Works of Art
Rugs, Tapestries
Silk Goods
Handmade Pottery
Chinaware
HORNE BUILDING
PHILADELPHIA

Fig. 1

JACQUILINE
Importer, Exporter
Rare Antiques
Oriental Works of Art
Rugs, Tapestries
Silk Goods
Handmade Pottery
Chinaware
HORNE BUILDING
PHILADELPHIA

Fig. 2

The designer has no occasion to worry about the appearance of one line of type beside its neighbor when the design is confined to a single style. With one style only, type harmony is obviously certain, and one of the main difficulties of the compositor is removed.

THE LAYOUT

PUBLICATION ADVERTISEMENT

SIZE: 7 in. by 10 in. deep

DISPLAY HEAD: Fashion orders Shuglors

TEXT: No definite amount of space has to be saved for the test, as the copy would be written after the layout has been completed.

CUT: Cut of a figure standing or walking. You may select the size cut you wish to use.

SUBHEAD: The Fashionable Shoe

CUT: 2 in. by 2 1/2 in. deep (Cut of a shoe)

SIGNATURE: Shuglors by Goodman

DIRECTIONS

1. Make three thumbnail sketches of the publication advertisement.

2. One color and black may be used.

3. Have the instructor check the sketches.

4. Make the finished layout.

5. Mark the layout for the compositor.

Unit 45   LETTERSPACING TYPE

Letterspacing is the placing of spaces between the letters. It is used chiefly in display lines of advertisements, on covers, running heads, title pages, etc. The purpose of letterspacing is to make the letters of a word combine so as to be easily read.   People read by glancing at words and recognizing the shape the combined letters form, and not by looking at each individual letter. Therefore, the manner in which letters combine to form word shapes regulates the ease with which the word can be recognized and read.

Lower-case letters do not have to be letterspaced, as the curved strokes of the letters allow enough white space between each letter, and the ascending and descending strokes give the words formed an uneven shape that is easily recognizable (Fig. 1). Caps are tall, erect and compact without ascenders and descenders to give the words shape. To aid in making cap lines easier to read, the words are quite often letterspaced (Fig. 1).

Do not letter space lower-case letters

Fig. 1

CAPS SET COMPACT   CAPS LETTERSPACED

Some typographers and layout men claim that all display words or lines set in capitals should be slightly letterspaced in order to equalize the space created by such combinations of letters as AY and AT. Straight letters as HE, IH and UI require more space between them than round letters such as DO, OC, etc. The compositor should endeavor to have the same amount of white space between all letters, regardless of the space between the serifs. The space between the letters forming words should be equalized to give the line a smooth, even tone (Fig. 2).

AVAILABLE LAWYERS   AVAILABLE LAWYERS
▲   ▲   ▲ ▲   ▲

Note the unequal space - especially where marked   *Letterspacing enables space to be equalized*

Fig. 2

Between capital L and capital T there will be found more space than between any other two letter combinations. In some composing rooms that specialize in fine advertising typography, it is no uncommon sight, especially in the larger sizes of type, to see all open letters as T, A, L, and Y mortised. (Mortising means the cutting away of a part of the body of the type.) For example, when a letter T follows an L, they will appear as in Fig. 3.

Fig. 3

In order to close the space between the two letters, the upper corner of the L is mortised, also a corner of the lower part of the T, so that the horizontal stroke of the T will extend into the white space at the top of the L. The two are thus brought closer together (Fig. 4).

Fig. 4

Where letterspacing is applied, the space between words should be increased slightly. Otherwise letterspacing will pull the words together, and it will be difficult to distinguish one word from another (Fig. 5).

Fig. 5

COMMON ERROR IN LETTERSP

This letterspaced line is difficult to read as the words run together

SPACE BETWEEN WORDS INCRE

When letterspacing a line of caps, the space between words should be increased.

THE LAYOUT

PROGRAM COVER

SIZE: 4 in. by 6 in. deep

COPY: Graduation Exercises
Industrial High School

DIRECTIONS

1. Make two thumbnail sketches of the program cover and submit them to the instructor.

2. One color and black may be used.

3. After the sketches have been checked by the instructor make the finished layout.

ASSIGNMENT PROBLEMS

DIRECTIONS

    A.   Write the answers to the following questions on a separate sheet of paper.

    B.   Have the answers checked by the instructor.

1. What is typefounding?

2. Name four metals that are combined to form the alloy that is used in making foundry type.

3. Which of the metals form the largest percentage of the type alloy?

4. Name the six type classifications.

5. What is the difference between oldstyle Roman and modern Roman?

6. Define each of the following: (a) type font (b) type family (c) type series.

7. Why is it better to use only one or two families of type on a printed piece, instead of five or six?

8. Why are words and lines set in caps letterspaced?

9. Should lower-case display lines be letterspaced? Explain.

10. Why should more space be placed between words in lines that are letterspaced than in lines that are set solid?

Unit 46   WORD SPACING

A layout man should always make sure that the compositor, when setting type, spaces the words so that the eye of the reader can follow each line with the least amount of effort. If an excessive amount of space is placed between words, a page or column of type may have white streaks running through the type mass. These white streaks are called "rivers" or "gutters" (Fig. 1).

Fig. 1

IF YOU WISH to lose friends and alienate people, suggest some bright morning that you would be happier in a world stripped of all its colors.

Note the "river" formed by wide word spacing in the type mass at the left, and the lack of the "rivers" in the type at the right.

Victor Keppler has lived with photography since he was nine — and now he has realized a passionate ambition. Convinced that there has too long been too much mystery about the taking, the

---

It is also possible to space words so closely together that it becomes a puzzle to the eye to determine where one word ends and the next one begins (Fig. 2).

Fig. 2

The art of spacing

Words spaced too closely make reading difficult

The art of spacing

3-to-em spaces make them easy to read

When spacing lower-case lines, the compositor should never place more than a 3-em space between words, and never less than a 5-em space. At times when the type is set in very narrow measures, the use of a 5-em space between words is permissible. Wide word spacing should not be used in setting short measures, as it makes white spots in the type composition and interferes with the readability of the type. Instead of the wide word spacing it is preferable to use thin letterspacing, but it must be done evenly throughout the entire line (Fig. 3). This is the only instance when the letterspacing of the lower case is desirable.

Fig. 3

Tympan has high tensile strength necessary to permit its being drawn tight on cylinder without danger of it stretching or tearing.

Tympan will stand up throughout gruelling grind of the longest runs. It will deliver the last impression as clear and sharp as the first.

Spaces between the words are too wide making the type mass spotty forming "rivers."

Thin letterspacing would improve the tone of the type mass and prevent "rivers"

Typesetters who desire to set fine typography vary the spacing between certain words because of the different shapes of letters. Tall letters, for example, like d, l and k, at the ending and beginning of words require more space between them than round letters like e and o in similar positions.

122

All words ending or starting with low characters such as e, m, c, a, o, r, u, s, z and x should have a 3-em space between them. Between all words ending and starting with high characters as dh, lk, fh, dt, etc., should be placed one 4-em and one 5-em space together. The combination of 4-em and 5-em spaces makes a space slightly wider than a 3-em space, and a little less than the en quad.

Letters like v and w seem to be wider apart when words end and start with them. Therefore, between words starting and ending with characters such as w, y, v, etc. a 4-em space should be placed. The same rules also apply to lines set in capitals.

Lines set in all caps require more space between words than do lower-case lines. If the line is not letterspaced, the en quad is usually placed between the words. When space is placed between the letters (letterspacing), then the space between the words should be increased (Fig. 4).

A COMMON ERROR IN LETTERSP

Fig. 4 *When letterspacing, the space between the words should be increased*

SPACE BETWEEN WORDS INCRE

Some compositors will place wide spacing between words at one end of a line and thin spacing at the other. This should be avoided because it produces a broken-up-uneven effect which will make the printing displeasing (Fig. 5).

This end too wide, this end too thin.

Line should be spaced evenly. from end to end.

Fig. 5

SPACING PUNCTUATION MARKS

A thin space should be placed between the word and a question mark, exclamation point, colon or semi-colon (Fig. 6).

Fig. 6

Display head?   Display head ?

Display head!   Display head !

Display head: Display head :

Spacing material has not been placed between the last letter and the punctuation marks.   *A thin space has been placed before the punctuation marks in the above lines.*

Between the opening quotes and the first word, a thin space should be inserted unless the first letter is an open letter (Fig. 7).

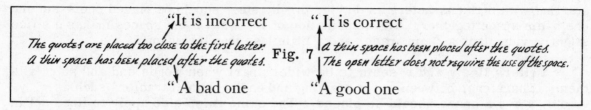

If the quotation marks in the closing quotes are preceded by a comma or period, the space should be omitted (Fig. 8).

Fig. 8

In spacing parens, the lower-case letters need no space between the letter and the paren, while a thin space should be placed between the capital letters and the parens (Fig. 9).

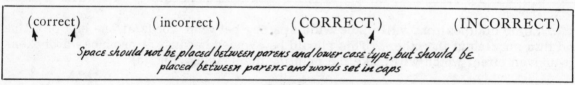

Fig. 9

USE OF RULE DASHES

In all cases the thickness of the dash is determined by the thickness of the type. Whenever a dash is set between words, a thin space should be placed between the dash and type on each side (Fig. 10). In some cases special em dashes containing space on each side are supplied by the type founders.

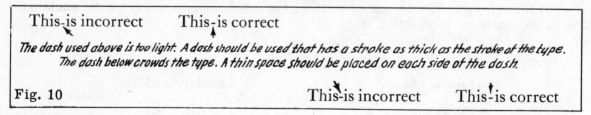

LINING UP INITIALS

Initials are used for two reasons. The first, or main purpose, is to draw the reader's attention to the beginning of the text, or to some other spot. The other is for decoration. Initials should never be emphasized and should never make the type composition spotty.

The two types of initials employed in typography are the stick-up initial and the sunken initial. Sunken initials should align at the top and down the left side with the rest of the line. If a three-line initial is used the bottom of the initial should align with the bottom of the third line (Fig. 11). The balance of the first word should be set in caps or small caps and placed as close to the initial as possible to make the word continuous. If the first word is composed of two or three letters, then the next one should also be capitalized. When the paragraph starts with a proper name, the whole name should be capitalized.

Fig. 11

EDUCATION is the backbone of all Prog-
ress — for things don't just happen.
Technical improvements can usually be

Incorrect. The bottom of the sunken initial should line up with the bottom of the second line.

NOT ONLY has the typographical
fad of bleed pages increased
the wastes in cutting and trim-
ming, and thrown the dimensional proportions of press sheets and mill sheets

Correct use of the sunken initial. Note how it lines up with the third line.

The stick-up initial must be aligned at the bottom with the type line. Open initials such as P, Y, F, V, W and T must be cut in so there is no space between the initial and the rest of the word (Fig. 12).

Fig. 12

The "A" does not align with the rest of the word, and there is too much space between the "A" and "R"

Incorrect →

A RE especially designed for
Mailpieces—these fine rag con

Note how the "T" aligns with the rest of the word and how it is cut in.

Correct →

THESE are difficult times.

THE LAYOUT

INVITATION CARD

SIZE: 5 in. by 3 1/2 in. deep

COPY: An Invitation

TEXT: We will display new Spring and Summer Frocks and
Hats in our English Room, Monday, March Second
at Two Thirty

SIGNATURE: McCall and Browning, Inc.
Oxford Street, Boston

DIRECTIONS

1. Make several thumbnail sketches of the invitation card.

2. One color and black may be used.

3. Without the aid of the instructor select the sketch you believe to be the best.

4. Make the finished layout, marking it for the compositor.

Unit 47   LINE SPACING

LEADING

Leading is the placing of space between the lines of type. Most leading is done with one or more 2-point metal strips called leads, although 1-point leads are used for small types. When 6 points or 12 points are desired between lines, a 6-point or 12-point slug is used instead of several leads.

Some type faces have short ascenders and descenders so the lines are grouped closely when set solid. In order to make the lines easier to read, leads are placed between the lines. Types with long ascenders and descenders have ample shoulder that admits enough white space between the lines so that leading is unnecessary.

There is no fixed rule for the right amount of leading. However, it is well to remember that the longer the line, the more need for leading (Fig. 1).

The most ancient materials employed for recording events were bricks, tiles, shells and tables of stone. The modes of writing on these different substances were various. The tiles and brick were impressed with a stamp when in a soft state; the shells and tables of stone were etched or graven, the figures or

The most ancient materials employed for recording events were bricks, tiles, shells and tables of stone. The modes of writing on these different substances were various. The tiles and brick were impressed with a stamp when in a soft state; the shells and tables of stone were etched or graven, the figures or

Fig. 1

Gothic and block types, having the width of their strokes all the same, form a dark mass of type when set solid (Fig. 2). Therefore, in order to aid in the readability of these types, it is necessary to place more space between the lines (Fig. 3).

Many factors enter into the choice of a type face besides legibility. One of the most important is weight or color. Some faces print light and some print dark; be-

Many factors enter into the choice of a type face besides legibility. One of the most important is weight or color. Some faces print light and some print dark; be-

Fig. 2   Fig. 3

LENGTH OF TYPE LINES

Type set in too narrow measures becomes difficult to read, and lines set in very wide measures make it difficult for the reader's eye to move from one end of a line to the beginning of the next (Fig. 4). In such instances, it is necessary for the designer to know the proper length of lines so that maximum eye comfort and pleasure can be given the reader.

Fig. 4

influential product of the printing art is books. There were countless books before the invention of printing, but let it be remembered that typography is merely time-saving inscribing, and that writing is man's most important invention. By that invention humanity was advanced from a limited

Scientists who have made a study of eye strain in relation to reading have found that a long line of large type can be read with greater ease than the same line set in small type. Other facts concerning type design and the readability of type have been found by experiments which today aid typographers and designers of type. Their findings enabled them to formulate a rule to the effect that the ideal length of a line may be secured by setting it the width of a lower case alphabet-and-a-half (39 lower case letters) of the type used (Fig. 5). It will not hinder the readability of the type if the lines are set a few characters more or less than the 39, but if the measure is increased considerably the leading must be increased proportionately to compensate for the additional width of the line (Fig. 6).

Fig. 5

The folder's surprise element jolts executives into a critical attitude towards their letterheads. Then the folder suggests a "desk-top laboratory" study of the customers' and other letterheads. Result: Each executive sells himself on needed changes. The folder also sells him on your ability to design and print letterheads that will make him swell his chest with justifiable pride.

The above column has been set about 39 characters wide. Note how easy it is to read.

Fig. 6

The type at the right has been set about 60 characters wide which makes it difficult to read. Space should be placed between the lines.

Fully comprehended it may open to a printer a vista of profound sentiment, and invest his occupation with a sacred character. The most influential product of the printing art is books. There were countless books before the invention of printing, but let it be remembered that typography is merely time-saving inscribing, and that writing is man's

The type at the right is set the same width as the group above. It is much easier to read as it has been leaded.

MATCHLESS in power among the arts of men is our art of printing. In its higher influence it is the chief servant of all that is divine in man. If we would, we may through printing types confer with all the choice spirits of preceding ages and learn all the knowledge acquired by men

PARAGRAPH ARRANGEMENT

Designers have available several popular methods of arranging paragraphs (Fig. 7). As there is no fixed rule to guide him, the layout man is free to use his own judgment as to which style he wishes to use on a printed page.

Fig. 7

Sunken Initial

HERE in America are the things which elsewhere in the world the nations stand in arms to conquer or to defend.

Flush Paragraph

Here in America are the things which elsewhere in the world the nations stand in arms to conquer or to defend.

Attention Spot

★ Here in America are the things which elsewhere in the world the nations stand in arms to conquer or to defend.

Hanging Indention

Here in America are the things which elsewhere in the world the nations stand in arms to conquer or to defend.

Raised Initial

HERE in America are the things which elsewhere in the world the nations stand in arms to conquer or to defend.

Indented paragraph

Here in America are the things which elsewhere in the world the nations stand in arms to conquer or to defend.

THE LAYOUT

MENU COVER

SIZE: 5 in. by 7 in. deep

COPY: Menu
Hotel Taft
Andy Jones and his Orchestra

DIRECTIONS

1. Make thumbnail sketches of the menu cover.

2. One color and black may be used.

3. Select the layout you believe to be the best and have it checked by the instructor.

4. Make the finished layout.

Unit 48   TYPE HARMONY

A printed page set in one family of type will always appear pleasing and harmonious because each member of the type family has similar characteristics. While it is wise for the beginner to use only one family of type as suggested in Unit 44, it is impossible for a designer to limit himself to the use of one family of type on every job. Therefore, a layout man should know how to select types that will harmonize.

In order to select types that will look pleasing when combined, it is necessary to study their characteristics. All types fall into one of six divisions (Fig. 1).

Fig. 1

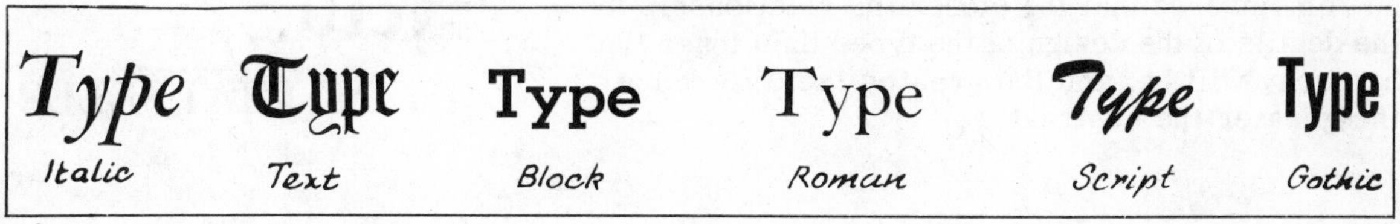

Italic   Text   Block   Roman   Script   Gothic

Some types have characteristics similar to others. The best harmony is secured when the two faces are similar. For example, Gothic types and block types are similar, since both have the strokes of the letters the same width throughout. Therefore, when Gothic and block types are combined there will be pleasing harmony (Fig. 2).

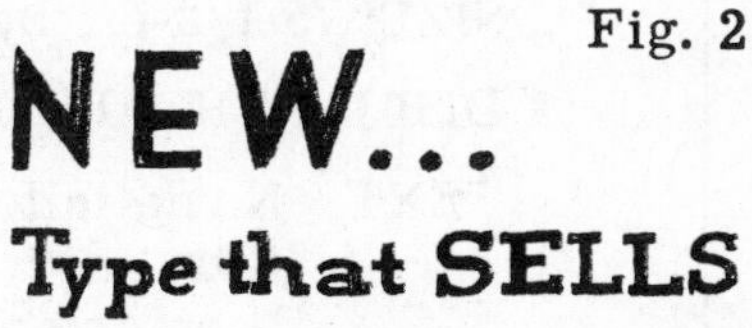

Gothic and block types will harmonize better than Gothic and Roman, because the Roman letters have thick and thin strokes which in no way resemble the strokes of the Gothic letters. The Roman types have small, thin, sharp-pointed serifs, while the Gothic types do not have serifs. Therefore, as they do not have similar characteristics, a combination of these types will not be harmonious (Fig. 3). Other combinations that have similar characteristics and harmonize are the Roman and italic, Roman and text, Roman and script, etc.

Script and italic are both on a slant, but script is an imitation of hand-writing, with letters joined, whereas the italic is a drawn letter. They have similar characteristics yet should not be used together, as each one is employed for the same purpose in a type composition. Both italic and script are used to accent certain parts of a printed page, so if one is employed for that purpose in a line the other should not be used (Fig. 4).

Fig. 2

NEW...
Type that SELLS

Fig. 3

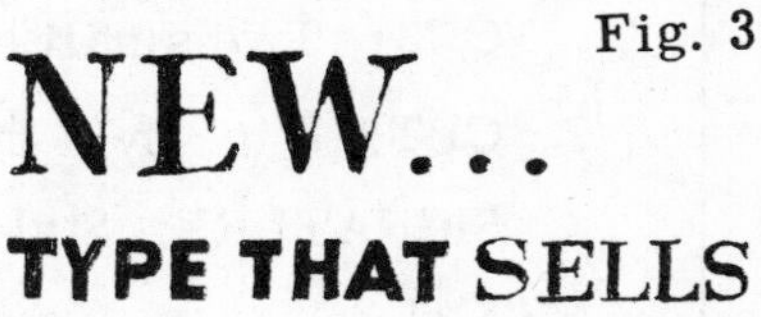

NEW...
TYPE THAT SELLS

Roman and Italic

New...
TYPE THAT *Sells*

Text and Gothic

New...
TYPE THAT Sells

129

The only time when types having similar characteristics should not be combined is when contrast is desired. By setting one or two words of a layout in type that does not have characteristics similar to that used in the rest of the layout, contrast is secured. For example, a page may be set in a Gothic type and the designer may wish to accent one or two words. If these words are set in a contrasting type such as a script, they will stand out more than the other words because their characteristics are different.

Therefore, when combining type, it should be remembered that the closer the relationship in the details of the design of the type, the closer the harmony will be; and the greater the difference, the greater the contrast.

Fig. 4

New...
type that Sells

New... Script and Block

TYPE THAT SELLS

New... Text and Roman

TYPE THAT SELLS

THE LAYOUT

PUBLICATION ADVERTISEMENT

SIZE: 5 1/2 in. by 11 1/2 in. deep

DISPLAY HEAD: Flair Fit guides your foot gracefully

TEXT: No definite amount of space is to be reserved for the text, as copy would be written after the layout has been completed.

CUT: Two small cuts of shoes, any size desired

CUT: 2 in. by 5 in. deep

SIGNATURE: Styl-eez, A Sellson Shoe

DIRECTIONS

1. Make several thumbnail sketches of the publication advertisement.

2. Have the instructor check the sketches.

3. Make the finished layout and mark it for the compositor

4. Make certain that the types selected harmonize.

REVIEW TEST

DIRECTIONS

    A.   On a separate sheet, complete the following sentences.

    B.   Have the instructor check the answers.

    C.   You are not allowed to speak to another student until after the test is completed.

1.   If there is placed an excessive amount of space between words, a page or column of type might have white streaks called _____ or _____ running through the type mass.

2.   Lower-case letters like ___, ___ and ___ at the ending and beginning of words require more space between them than letters like ____ and ____ in similar positions.

3.   Lines set in all caps require _____ space between words than do lower-case lines.

4.   A _____ space should be placed between the word and a question mark, exclamation point, colon and semi-colon.

5.   The difference between a lead and a slug is _____

6.   The ideal length to set lines in order to have them easily read is _____ _____ of the type used.

7.   If types selected to be used together on a printed page have _____ _____ they will harmonize.

8.   The metal used to harden the alloy forming type is _____

9.   The size of wood type is designated by _____ instead of point.

10. The parts of a piece of type are _____ , _____ , _____ , _____ , _____ , _____ , _____ , _____ , _____ and _____ .

Unit 49   CAPS, LOWER CASE AND ITALIC

The capital was derived from the inscriptions cut in stone on walls and arches of ancient Roman cities. On buildings today the capital is used for the same purpose, and anything else looks out of place. Hence today, nothing better has been found for titles, headings and formal printing.

When there is considerable reading matter, it is not a good policy to use capitals alone, because words set in caps are not so easy to read as words set in lower case. If it is necessary to set several lines of caps, they should be well leaded, since it is difficult to read capital lines that are closely spaced.

The varying widths and heights of the different characters make lower-case letters much clearer and easier to read than capitals. Before children can spell they are able to read by remembering how the words appear rather than spelling out the letters. A word set in lower case has more shape than the same word set in caps; therefore as we recognize the word by its shape it is only logical that the words having the most shape are the ones easiest to read. Lower-case letters, with the ascenders and descenders giving the words uneven shapes, will form words that are read with greater ease and speed than words printed in caps (Fig. 1).

VOICE TO THE   **voice to the**

Notice that the words set in caps do not form as irregular a shape as the words in lower case.

Fig. 1

The lines set in lower case is easier to read than the lines in caps as the letters form irregular shapes.

GIVING VOICE TO THE COUNTLESS THO
giving voice to the countless thousands wh

When italic was first designed, its purpose was to conserve space, but today it is not used with this purpose in mind. We use it when we wish to accent a certain word or line.

Capitals appear straight and erect, with a dignity not found in lower-case letters. In display, the use of all capitals produces a formal composition. Professional business cards, formal announcements, etc. are given dignity by the use of all capitals, and advertisements set in all caps appear formal and dignified (Fig. 2).

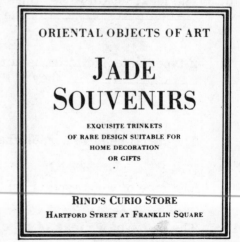

ORIENTAL OBJECTS OF ART

JADE SOUVENIRS

**EXQUISITE TRINKETS
OF RARE DESIGN SUITABLE FOR
HOME DECORATION
OR GIFTS**

RIND'S CURIO STORE
HARTFORD STREET AT FRANKLIN SQUARE

Fig. 2

Lower case is easier to read than caps but does not appear as dignified. Lower case is ideal for lengthy display heads and text matter (Fig. 3).

Words or lines should never be set completely in caps if script or text types are employed. A word set in text or script caps is very difficult to read, so it is a common practice among designers to retain lower case when text or script types are used (Fig. 4). Capitals should be used only as the first letter of a word at the beginning of a sentence and with words which need to be capitalized.

In the greater portion of display work, it is best to use a combination of caps, lower case and italic in order to give the display variety and emphasis. Some designers insist upon using all caps or all lower case, but they are thinking more of the beauty of the advertisement than of its readability and expressiveness. Men who use lower case with a few lines of capitals have sacrificed nothing as far as beauty and dignity are concerned. Combining the two gives variety to the printed piece as well as expressiveness (Fig. 5).

Fig. 3 *Lower case is ideal for lengthy display heads and text matter.*

PRINTER
Printer

Fig. 4

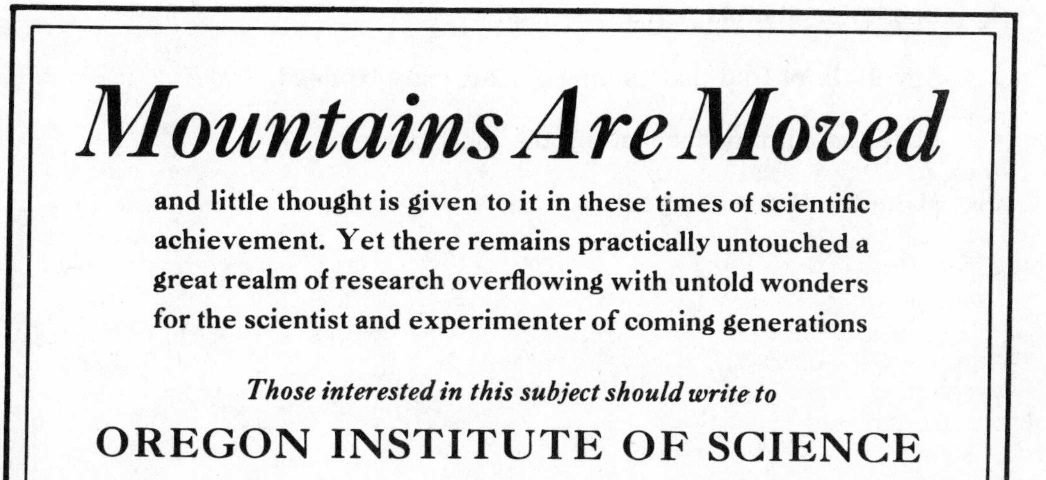

Fig. 5

Summarizing, caps give a page a dignified and formal appearance. Lower case is easier to read than caps, and italic attracts attention to words or lines when used with caps and lower case. Printing set in a combination of caps, lower case and italic is much more expressive than the use of all caps or all lower case.

THE LAYOUT

FOLDER

SIZE: 4 in. by 6 in. deep (when folded)

COVER COPY: The Wayside presents....

INSIDE COPY:

HEAD: The Best Food in New England

TEXT: Any amount of space desired may be reserved for the text.

CUT: 2 in. by 2 in. deep

SIGNATURE: The Wayside Lounge
Milford, Connecticut

DIRECTIONS

1. Make a rough dummy of the folder.

2. One color and black may be used.

3. Any style of fold that is appropriate may be used.

4. Have the dummy checked by the instructor.

5. Make the finished layout.

Unit 50   SELECTION OF TYPE

Every year the type founders design and manufacture new type faces to be used by layout men and typesetters. The continual addition of new type designs makes it possible for some designers and compositors to have a large selection of type available. However, the person having a large assortment of type to work with may become confused and make poor type selections. Therefore, it is necessary to have some method of selecting type for printed pieces.

At times it is very easy to make a type selection because a trade mark or signature may control the choice. For example, if a concern has a trade mark containing lettering with all the strokes the same width, it would be appropriate to select a Gothic type so that the type and trade mark would harmonize (Fig. 1).

Fig. 1   *The type has been selected to harmonize with the trademark*

It is not always possible to select type in this manner, therefore, another method is employed by some designers. In this method all types are divided into six classifications, and ways of using the type are suggested as follows:

ALL-PURPOSE TYPE

Many factors enter into the choice of a type face besides legibility. One of the most important is weight or color. Some faces print light and some print dark; between the ex-

Caslon

Many factors enter into the choice of a type face besides legibility. One of the most important is weight or color. Some faces print light and some print dark; between the ex-

Binney

Many factors enter into the choice of a type face besides legibility. One of the most important is weight or color. Some faces print light and some print dark; between the ex-

Bookman

Fig. 2

Caslon, Bookman, Binny Old Style and Ronaldson are types that may be used on all jobs quite successfully. When there is doubt about the selection of type for a job, one of the ALL-PURPOSE types may be appropriately used. "When in doubt use Caslon," is an old saying that has been repeated by printers for years.

FORMAL TYPE

Bodoni, Bulmer, Baskerville, Scotch Roman, Corvinus and types with similar characteristics of design that appear very straight and erect are constructed with thick stems and extremely thin hairlines. Therefore, they should be used with cuts that have sharp contrasting darks and lights, and cuts of stiff, straight mechanical articles such as machines. They are ideal to use with sharp pen and ink illustrations and very appropriate on coated papers, since these papers have a smooth, hard surface that harmonizes with the hardness and stiffness of the type. These formal types are also ideal for financial, legal and educational work commonly prepared for doctors, dentists, lawyers and schools.

Fig. 3

Many factors enter into the choice of a type face besides legibility. One of the most important is weight or color. Some faces print light and some print dark; be-

Bodoni Bold

Many factors enter into the choice of a type face besides legibility. One of the most important is weight or color. Some faces print light and some print dark; between the extremes of very

Bulmer

Many factors enter into the choice of a type face besides legibility. One of the most important is weight or color. Some faces print light and some print dark; between the extremes of very

Egmont Bold

Many factors enter into the choice of a type face besides legibility. One of the most important is weight or color. Some faces print light and some print dark; between the extremes of very

Corvinus Medium

Many factors enter into the choice of a type face besides legibility. One of the most important is weight or color. Some faces print light and some print dark; between the extremes of very

Baskerville Bold

Many factors enter into the choice of a type face besides legibility. One of the most important is weight or color. Some faces print light and some print dark; between the extremes of very

Scotch Roman

INFORMAL TYPE

Many factors enter into the choice of a type face besides legibility. One of the most important is weight or color. Some faces print light and some print dark; between the ex-

Goudy

Many factors enter into the choice of a type face besides legibility. One of the most important is weight or color. Some faces print light and some print dark; between the extremes of very light and

Garamond

Many factors enter into the choice of a type face besides legibility. One of the most important is weight or color. Some faces print light and some print dark; be-tween the extremes of very light and very

Cloister

Many factors enter into the choice of a type face besides legibility. One of the most important is weight or color. Some faces print light and some print dark; between the extremes of

Cochin

Fig. 4

Types that are freely designed with numerous curves such as Goudy, Garamond, Cloister, Nicolas Cochin, etc. are called informal types. These types should be used with cuts that are light in tone or color and drawn with sketchy, curved lines. They are ideal with vignette halftones and decorative borders.

MODERN TYPES

Many factors enter into the choice of a type face besides legibility. One of the most important is weight or color. Some faces print light and some print dark; between the extremes of very

Sans Serif Medium

Many factors enter into the choice of a type face besides legibility. One of the most important is weight or color. Some faces print light and some print dark; between the ex-

Stymie Medium

Many factors enter into the choice of a type face besides legibility. One of the most important is weight or color. Some faces print light and some print dark; between the extremes of very

Franklin Gothic

Many factors enter into the choice of a type face besides legibility. One of the most important is weight or color. Some faces print light and some print dark; between the extremes of very

Futura Medium

Fig. 5

Bernhard Gothic, Phenix, Stymie, Franklin Gothic and all types with the strokes of the letters the same width are modern types. These types are appropriate for use on coated papers, brightly colored papers or on blocks of color. They are exceptionally good on gold or silver backgrounds. Lines of type that are to be re-versed should be set in modern types. Printing arranged in the modern manner should also employ these types.

RUGGED, POWERFUL TYPES

Cooper Black   Stymie Black   Hobo BROADWAY

Fig. 5

The rugged types are Cooper, Stymie Black, Hobo, Broadway and other faces that are extra black. These types should be used on printing that needs to express the feeling of power, strength or ruggedness. They are ideal on printing for sales and grocery or butcher advertisements. Because of their wide strokes they are excellent on brightly colored stocks or tint blocks.

Trafton Script
Park Avenue   HUXLEY VERTICAL   *Kaufmann*   *Legend*
                                      PERICLES   *Elegante*

Fig. 6

Decorative, unusual types, such as Trafton Script, Huxley Vertical, Kaufmann, Romany, Park Avenue, Pericles, etc., are known as occasional types. They are used to make the advertisement a little "prettier" and to accent certain words. These types should be used in only one or two places in an advertisement.

THE LAYOUT

TICKET

SIZE: 3 in. by 1 5/8 in.

COPY: Annual Dinner Dance
The Elks Club
Saturday, June 12th
Admission: $2.00 Tax $.20   Total $2.20 a couple

DIRECTIONS

1. Make two thumbnail sketches of the ticket, arranging it in the modern manner.

2. One color and black may be used.

3. Select the thumbnail sketch you believe to be the better.

4. Make the finished layout.

5. Have the instructor check the finished layout.

Unit 51   COPYFITTING

When arranging printed matter, it is necessary for the layout man to know the amount of space he must save in the layout for the text. If the correct amount of space is not reserved, the compositor may have trouble when setting the type. The space saved in the layout may be too small for the amount of copy and would force the printer to crowd the type or set it in a smaller size. At times there is not enough copy to fill the space saved by the layout man, so the printer has to make adjustments which may spoil the appearance of the printed page.

To avoid trouble, most layout men take time to figure mathematically the amount of space the text will occupy. Many systems have been devised for copy-fitting, but there apparently is only one accurate way of casting copy and that is by the character count method.

Let us assume that the typewritten copy (Fig. 1) is to be set in a column 12 picas wide. In order to reserve the correct amount of space in the layout it will be necessary to figure the depth the column will be when the type is set. Before starting to copyfit this typewritten matter, the layout man should select a good body type for it to be set in and then decide upon the type size and amount of leading that should be placed between each line. For example: 10-point Goudy Catalog leaded 2 points might be the selection. Then to find the amount of space it will occupy in a 12 pica column, proceed step by step as suggested below:

PROCEDURE

1.   Find the number of characters in the first line of the typewritten copy (Fig. 1) that will occupy one inch. Count each space and punctuation mark as a character.

Line 1 →	29 Characters
2 →	28
3 →	28
4 →	27
5 →	28
6 →	29
7 →	32
8 →	29
9 →	31
10 →	29
11 →	33
12 →	59
13 →	59
14 →	53

494 characters
The number of type-written characters in the copy.

According to the 1955 Census, 29
printing ranks first on four 28
points: number of establish- 28
ments, value added by manu- 27
facture, salaried employees, 28
and salaries. The Department 29
of Commerce also places printing 32
first among all industries in 29
Philadelphia, Boston, San Fran- 31
cisco, and Washington; second 29
in New York, Chicago, Los Angeles 33
and St. Louis; and third in Detroit and Cincinnati. In Los 59
Angeles the printing volume was only a million dollars less 59
than that of the celebrated moving picture interests. 53

2. Measure the length of the first line of the typewritten copy in inches (Fig. 1) and multiply by the number of characters contained in one inch.

There are 10 typewritten characters in one inch. The first line is 2⅞" and has 29 characters (Note figures under the ruler in Fig.1)

3. In the same manner find the number of characters in each line and then add them to find the number of characters in the copy.

There are 494 characters in the typewritten copy. (Note the addition of the characters in the space beside fig.1)

4. Secure a sample of the type (Fig. 2) the copy is to be set in and count the number of type characters that will set in the 12 pica column width.

30 type characters will set in 12 picas. (Note the method of counting as illustrated in Fig.2)

Fig. 2

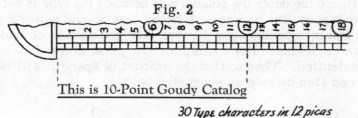

This is 10-Point Goudy Catalog

30 Type characters in 12 picas

5. Divide the number of characters in the typewritten copy by the number of type characters in the column width. This will give the number of lines that will have to be set.

$$\begin{array}{r} 16.4 \text{ or } 17 \text{ lines} \\ 30\overline{)494.0} \\ \underline{30} \\ 194 \\ \underline{180} \\ 140 \end{array}$$

Number of characters in copy

Copy will be set in 17 lines

6. Add the point size of the type and the amount of space (leading) that is to be placed between each line. The result will give the amount of space in points that one line will occupy.

$$\begin{array}{r} 10 \text{ point type} \\ + \ 2 \text{ point leading} \\ \hline 12 \text{ points...} \end{array}$$
amount of space each line will occupy

7. Multiply the amount of space one line occupies by the number of lines it will take to set the copy. This will give the amount of space in points that it will take to set the copy.

$12 \times 17 = 204 \text{ pts.}$ — *Am't space needed to set copy*

Space in pts. one line occupies   *Number of lines to be set*

8. Find the depth of the column in picas by dividing the number of points in the depth by 12. This will give the space the copy will occupy (Fig. 3).

$$\begin{array}{r} 17 \text{ picas} \\ 12\overline{)204} \\ \underline{12} \\ 84 \\ \underline{84} \end{array}$$

Number of points in one pica

It will take a space 12 picas by 17 picas deep to set the copy in Fig.1

Thus we see that the typewritten copy (Fig. 1) when set in 10-point Goudy (Fig. 2), leaded 2 points, will occupy a space 12 picas wide and 17 picas deep (Fig. 3).

Fig. 3

According to the 1955 Census, printing ranks first on four points: number of establishments, value added by manufacture, salaried employees, and salaries. The Department of Commerce also places printing first among all industries in Philadelphia, Boston, San Francisco, and Washington; Second in New York, Chicago, Los Angeles and St. Louis; and third in Detroit and Cincinnati. In Los Angeles the printing volume was only a million dollars less than that of the celebrated moving picture interests.

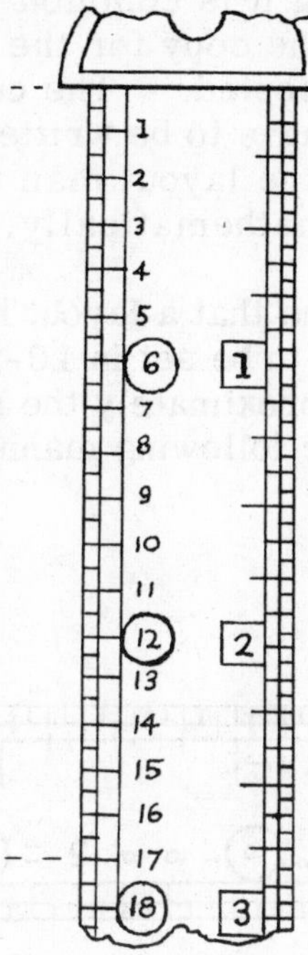

THE LAYOUT

SIZE: 4 in. by 6 in. deep

DISPLAY HEAD: Announcing New Exhibitions

TEXT: Our many members will be pleased to hear that we have arranged for numerous extraordinarily beautiful exhibits this year. The vast field of advertising typography has been fine-combed for the most outstanding specimens. Several of the country's leading typographers will be present to address the members.

SIGNATURE: Graphic Arts Club
New York City

DIRECTIONS

1. Make several small sketches of the copy and have the instructor check them.

2. Make a rough layout of the copy the size the finished job is to be made.

3. Select an appropriate type and figure the amount of space it will take to set the text.

4. Make the finished layout and mark it completely for the compositor.

Unit 52   COPYFITTING NO. 2

In advertising it is common practice to write only the display lines before a layout is made. The copy for the text would, in such cases, be written after the layout has been accepted. The copywriter must know approximately the number of words that will have to be written to fill the space allotted for the text. It would be impossible for the layout man to guess correctly in every case so it would be safer to figure it mathematically.

Let us assume that a layout has a space 12 picas wide by 24 picas deep (Fig. 1), and the copy is to be set in 10-point Goudy Bold leaded 4 points. It would be possible to find approximately the number of words that would have to be written to fill the space in the following manner.

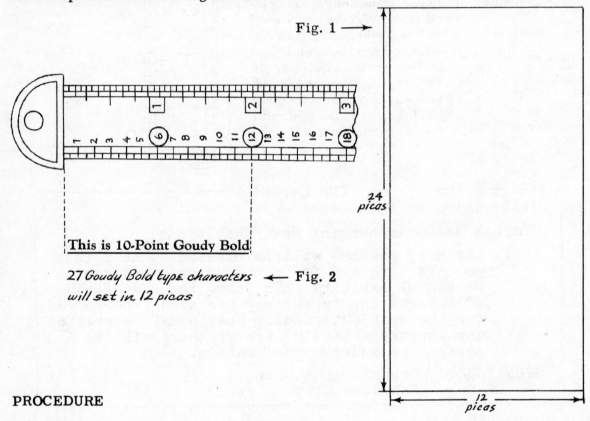

Fig. 1 ——→

This is 10-Point Goudy Bold

27 Goudy Bold type characters ←— Fig. 2
will set in 12 picas

24
picas

12
picas

PROCEDURE

1. Find the depth of the column in points.

    24 picas x 12 pts. = 288 points

2. Find the number of points one line will occupy by adding the point size of the type and the leading used between each line.

    10 points – size of type
    + 4 points – am't of leading
    14 points – am't of space
    each line will occupy

3. Find the number of lines that will set into the space by dividing the number of points in the depth of the column by the number of points one line will occupy.

    20.5 or 21 lines
    14)288.0
    28
    80
    70

    Space each line occupies ↑   Depth of col. →

4.   Count the number of type characters (Fig. 2) that will set into the width of the column (Fig. 1). Count each punctuation mark and each space between words as one character.

} *27 Goudy Bold type characters will set in the width of the column (See Fig.2)*

5.   In order to find the number of characters that will set into the space or column, multiply the number that will set into one line by the number of lines.

}
$$27 \rightarrow \text{\textit{Number of characters in one line}}$$
$$\underline{21} \rightarrow \text{\textit{Number of lines}}$$
$$27$$
$$\underline{54}$$
$$567 \text{ \textit{characters will set in the}}$$
12 pica by 24 pica column.

6.   It has been found by actual count that the average word contains 5 1/2 characters. Therefore, in order to find the number of words that would have to be written to fill the space, divide the number of characters the space will hold by 5 1/2 (Fig. 3).

}
$$103.09 \text{ or } \textit{103 words would}$$
$$5.5\overline{)567.0.00} \quad \textit{have to be written}$$
$$\underline{55} \qquad\qquad \textit{to occupy the}$$
$$170 \qquad\quad \textit{12} \times \textit{24 pica space.}$$
$$\underline{165}$$
$$500$$
$$\underline{495}$$

ASSIGNMENT PROBLEM

Find the number of words that would have to be written to fill a column 14 picas wide and 18 picas deep. The type will be set in 10-point Goudy leaded 4 points.

THE LAYOUT

COPY

SIZE: 4 in. by 6 in. deep

DISPLAY HEAD: Proof....beyond a doubt

TEXT: No definite amount of space has to be reserved for the text since it will be copyfitted and the copy written after the layout has been completed.

SIGNATURE: Call TOOF for proof
Phone 236, Akron, Ohio

DIRECTIONS

1.   Make two thumbnail sketches of the copy.

2.   Have the instructor check the sketches and aid in selecting the better one.

3.   Make the finished layout.

4.   Mark the layout for the compositor.

5.   Select an appropriate type for the text and figure the number of words that would have to be written to fill the space that you have reserved for the text.

SECTION III — REVIEW

DIRECTIONS

    A. On a separate sheet, answer the following questions.

    B. Have the instructor check the answers.

1. Why are lower-case letters easier to read than caps?

2. When italic was first designed, its purpose was to conserve space. Why is it used today?

3. In order to give a small business card a dignified professional appearance, should it be set in caps, lower case or italic?

4. Why is it best when setting display composition to use a combination of caps, lower case and italic?

5. Name a type face that can be used appropriately on any job.

6. What type face could be used appropriately with a line cut of a machine that has been drawn with sharp contrasting pen lines?

7. What type would be appropriate to use on a gold cover stock?

8. Figure the number of words that have to be written to fill a column 12 picas wide by 30 picas deep if it were set solid in 10-point Caslon Oldstyle.

9. What is a matrix?

10. Which would be better to use on antique paper, oldstyle or modern Roman type?

11. Make a sketch of the following characters that might be in a font of type: asterisk, paragraph mark, double dagger.

12. When letterspacing, why should not the same amount of space be placed between each letter?

13. Why should a column of 12-point type set 18 picas wide be leaded more than a column set 10 picas?

14. What is a hanging indention?

15. Why should lower-case italic and script not be used in the same line?

16. Why are script types used in advertisements?

17. What are "rivers" and how can they be avoided?

18. What metal is used in the largest percentage for the alloy that forms type metal?

19. Why are types made of wood?

Section IV

Color

Unit 53   INTRODUCTION TO COLOR

Each year more color is being used in the printing of magazines, catalogues and other types of commercial work. It has been proved that advertisements in color increase sales ten and fifteen times more than the same advertisements in black and white. Color attracts attention, creates interest, and allows products, trademarks and other features to be printed in their natural colors.

Color is a part of the printer's business, and since more color is being used each year, it becomes essential that the printer know color and how to use it.

COLOR AND LIGHT

Color is the effect produced when the rays of light from the sun are reflected from objects. Some objects reflect the colors of the sun's rays, while other objects absorb the colors. We see the reflected colors, while the absorbed colors are not visible. That is the reason all objects are not the same color. The eye is capable of seeing only the three colors red, yellow and blue, which, when blended together, will form the other commonly known colors. Therefore, a piece of blue paper will absorb all rays except the blue ray which is reflected so that the paper will appear blue to the eye. A sheet of green paper will absorb the red rays and reflect the yellow and blue which will combine and blend together to form green.

If a piece of blue paper is taken into a room where there is no light it will not appear blue. This shows that without light the presence of color cannot be seen or appreciated.

Some books on physics do not agree that the three colors contained in light are red, yellow and blue. They claim that blue, green and red are the three basic colors contained in light, as these three colors when mixed in the proper proportions will produce the other hues. Some psychology textbooks claim that red, yellow, green and blue are the basic colors contained in light. These theories are of little value to the printer, as it has been found that when working with printing ink, the three colors that form other hues are red, yellow and blue.

PRIMARY COLORS

Red, yellow and blue are called the primary colors (Fig. 1) because they are the colors which form all other colors and are the only colors which cannot be obtained by mixing other colors. A printer who has red, yellow and blue inks therefore, should be able to mix any other color he wishes to use.

Fig. 1

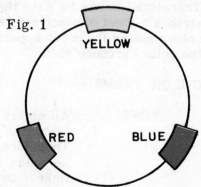

145

SECONDARY COLORS

By combining any two of the primary colors, a secondary color will be formed (Fig. 2). These secondary colors are violet (blue and red), green (yellow and blue) and orange (red and yellow).

TERTIARY AND OTHER COLORS

The primary and secondary colors are the best known and most popular colors in printing, yet other less popular colors can be formed from the primaries and secondaries. By combining any two secondary colors, a third or tertiary (pronounced tur' she-a-ry) color may be formed (Fig. 3). The tertiary colors are russet (orange and violet), citrine (orange and green) and olive (green and violet).

In addition to the primary, secondary and tertiary colors, other hues can be formed. Colors may be formed by combining primary and secondary colors such as red and orange, blue and green, violet and red, blue and violet, and so forth. These combinations are called intermediate colors (Fig. 4).

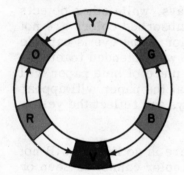

Fig. 2 SECONDARY

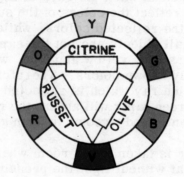

Fig. 3 TERTIARY

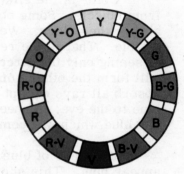

Fig. 4 INTERMEDIATE

BLACK AND WHITE

Black and white are not commonly spoken of as colors. Theoretically, black is the absence of color and white is the presence of all colors. A person entering a dark room sees no color, as there are no light rays in the room and color comes from light. As there are no light or color rays, everything in the room is black. Therefore, it can be said that black is the absence of color. When a ray of light strikes a sheet of paper and reflects all of the colors, the presence of all the reflected colors makes the paper appear white. Theoretically, the presence and blending of all the colors produce white.

COLOR TERMS

TONE...... All colors may be darkened or lightened by adding a small amount of black or white ink, whichever changes the tone. Therefore, when we say the tone of a color should be changed, we mean that the color should be made either darker or lighter by the addition of black or white.

HUE........If a color is added to another color the result is called a hue. For example, a green ink may be changed to a hue of green by the addition of blue, or any other color.

SHADE.....A shade of a color is formed by the addition of black to the color. If, instead of using the green now employed, a shade of green is preferred, the green should be darkened by the addition of black.

TINT.......It might be desirable to have a color changed to a tint. In order to make the change, white would be mixed with the color. Therefore, white mixed with a color forms a tint of the color. When mixing white and a color, it is always best to add the color to the white instead of the white to the color.

INTENSITY..The intensity of a color is its brilliance, power and full strength. To say that a color should be in its full intensity means that it should be as strong, bright and pure as possible.

THE LAYOUT

COPY (A) PROGRAM COVER

SIZE: 4 in. by 6 in. deep

COPY: Alumni Dinner
Industrial High School

COPY (B) CATALOGUE COVER

SIZE: 4 in. by 6 in. deep

COPY: Ayerson Aviation School
Entrance Requirements

DIRECTIONS

1. Select either copy (A) or copy (B) and make at least two thumbnail sketches.

2. One color and black may be used.

3. Have the instructor select the better sketch.

4. Make the finished layout, indicating the color on the layout with a colored pencil.

Unit 54   COLOR PREFERENCES

It has been determined by actual tests among men and women that their personal color preferences are as follows:

PREFERENCES OF MEN

Of the pure colors, men like blue first, then red, violet, green, orange and yellow. When shades of the colors are formed, the order changes slightly with blue first, then violet, red, green, orange and yellow. The tints of the colors are preferred by men in the same order as the pure colors except that orange is last and yellow is next to last in preference.

PREFERENCES OF WOMEN

Red is the first choice of women when pure colors are employed, with blue second, then violet, green, orange and yellow. When shades of the colors are formed, the women prefer violet first, then blue, green, red, orange and yellow. Among tints the feminine preference is for violet, yellow, green, orange and red.

From the above preferences it can be noticed that red is a color that is favored when in its pure form, but is not popular when in tints and shades. Yellow, as a pure color and in shades ranks lowest but has more appeal when used in tints. Blue is the one color that is appealing in all tones and violet is preferred in its tints and shades.

OTHER PREFERENCE FACTORS

Color has a different effect upon different people according to their age and education. Printing that is to be read by children or uneducated people should be printed in pure, brilliant colors. As a person becomes older, soft tones of color are more appealing. It seems that young people prefer loud music and bright colors while older persons like soft music and soft colors.

COLOR SELECTION

DISTANT READING

A successful printed piece must be arranged so that the type is easy to read. When type is to be printed in color and is to be read at a distance, the most readable combination is black on yellow, then green on white, blue on white and black on white. These combinations pertain to large jobs, such as posters that are to be read from a distance. In printing jobs to be read at arms length, these combinations are not important. For normal reading, type matter printed in color should be dark.

COOL AND WARM COLORS

Colors are classified into two groups known as warm colors and cool colors. The colors that have always been associated with the appearance of fire, sunshine and the sun are red, yellow and orange. These are called the warm colors.

Violet, blue and dark green are called cool colors because they seem to produce a cool sensation to the observer. If a printed piece were to be created for a summer camp or a cool drink, the best choice of colors would be those that are considered cool colors. On the other hand, a warm color would be a wise selection if the printed piece were to advertise an oil burner.

Very pleasing results can be obtained by using warm colors with cool colors. A dark cool color and a light warm color will give pleasing results if the colors are two that harmonize. The same amount of cool colors and warm colors should not be used on a job, but a small amount of warm color would be better if used with a large amount of a cool color.

BACKGROUND COLORS

Some colors appear closer to a person than others. For example, notice how much closer a red traffic light looks than a green one. The warm colors appear to advance while the cool colors recede. Therefore, the cool colors in most cases make better background colors for type than the warm colors, as they appear to stay in the background, making the type more pronounced.

COLOR SELECTION CONSIDERATIONS

When selecting a color for a printed piece, a few other points should be considered by the printer before a final selection is made:

1. A color that is appropriate should be selected for the job. It would be a poor policy to use blue and black on an advertisement for fire trucks when red is the color the average person thinks of in relation to fire, firemen and fire trucks. Therefore, red and black would be a better choice.

2. Do not use the same color or colors as your customer's competitor does on his advertising.

3. If an object that is naturally a certain color is to be printed, do not for any reason print in another color. In using color advertising containing a cut of a lemon, it is necessary to print the cut in yellow, the color recognized as natural for lemons.

CHARACTERISTICS OF COLOR

RED - Red is a bold and powerful color, and very appealing. If used too often or in too great a quantity as a second color, red becomes commonplace. It will be found that a single spot or line of red will be enough to catch the eye.

Red is not a good background color when overprinted with black, especially if the red is a dark shade. The black type on the red background will not be legible. Red as a background color is very appropriate if the type is reversed (white letter with a red background). Small sizes of type and lightface type should not be reversed on red.

149

YELLOW - Yellow is the color of light and the sun. It is a very brilliant color and when used as a background color for black, or as a yellow letter on black, it is easily read at a distance. It should always be used in a large mass and never as type matter on white stock. The yellow letter is too near white in tone to be easily read.

The reversing of type on a yellow background also should be avoided. The white letters on the yellow background will not form a strong enough contrast to allow the type to be easily read.

ORANGE - People associate orange with gold. It is brilliant and suggests wealth, prosperity and happiness. This color in its pure form should be used in the same manner as yellow. The shade of orange (brown) can be used in practically any manner, is one of the easiest colors to use, and is one of the most popular colors used by printers.

GREEN - Green is the color of nature. As nature is genuine, green suggests sincerity. It is a color that is appropriate for use on almost any piece of printed matter. This is truer of green than of any other color except brown. These two colors may be used in large or small areas.

VIOLET - Violet is symbolic of splendor, royalty and pomp. It is the color of night, darkness and is a calming, soothing color. Violet is not used by printers and layout men as much as it could be. It is an easy color to use, as it is a good ornamental color for borders, initials and so on, and is also a color that is legible when used as type on white stock.

Tints or shades of violet, used in large areas, form a very good background color for type, either printed on the color or reversed. If black type is to be printed on a violet background, the violet should be light and the type large in size. The tints of violet (lavender) appeal to women and can be used appropriately on printed matter which should have feminine appeal, but they prove to be unsatisfactory to use on a printed piece advertising men's suits.

BLUE - Blue is symbolic of the sky and water. It represents patience, hope and quietness. It is the favorite color of the majority of people, so the printer can feel quite safe in using this color. Blue is a color that is appealing in both its tints and shades. It is a very good background color, as type can be easily read when reversed (white letter on blue background) or when printed on the blue. When black type is printed on blue, the color should be very light or it will be difficult to read the words.

THE LAYOUT

MAILING CARD

SIZE: 5 1/2 in. by 3 1/4 in. deep

DISPLAY HEAD: A New Boys' Camp

TEXT: Mr. James C. Walton wishes to announce that his new camp on Cape Cod will be open for the coming season. You will receive a catalog in the near future.

SIGNATURE: Camp Pinecape
On Historic Cape Cod

DIRECTIONS

1. Make at least two thumbnail sketches of the mailing card.

2. One appropriate color besides black may be used.

3. Have the sketches checked by the instructor.

4. Make the finished layout, indicating the color on the layout with a colored pencil.

Unit 55   THE PRINTER'S COLOR WHEEL

...king with color, the layout men and printers do not guess at color ... hoping they will look pleasing together, but instead make their selections ...r wheel. The purpose of this unit is to explain the construction of the ...el, and following units will explain the methods of using the wheel to select colo... ombinations that harmonize.

As the three primary colors are red, yellow and blue, they are used as the foundation of the color wheel. Therefore, place them in a triangular position as in Fig. 1.

When yellow and red are mixed together they form orange. Place orange halfway between the yellow and red on the triangle (Fig. 2).

Place green between the yellow and blue, and violet between red and blue (Fig. 2).

To complete the color wheel the intermediate colors should be placed as in Fig. 3.

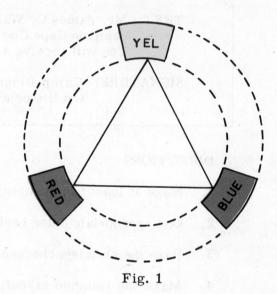

Fig. 1

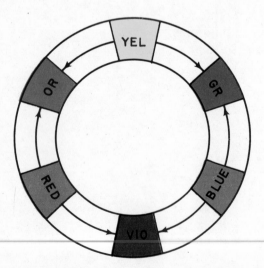

Fig. 2

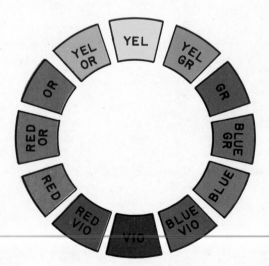

Fig. 3

ASSIGNMENT PROBLEMS

DIRECTIONS

A. Write the answers to the following questions on a separate sheet of paper.

B. After completing the work, have the instructor check the answers.

1. Name the three primary colors.

2. What two primary colors, when mixed together, will form violet?

3. When red and yellow inks are mixed together, what color will be formed?

4. What two colors, when mixed together, will form blue?

5. Name the secondary colors.

6. What would have to be added to a green ink to form a shade of green?

7. If someone told you to use a color in its full intensity, what would he mean?

8. What would have to be added to a green ink to form a tint of green?

9. Of the pure colors, which one do the majority of men like best?

10. If a printed piece advertising milk were to be designed to appeal to children, what colors would be best to use? Why?

11. What colors appeal to older and better educated people?

12. Which of the pure colors do women prefer?

13. If one color besides black were to be used on a poster which is to be read from a long distance, what color would be the best choice?

14. What color would you select to use with black on a printed piece advertising an oil burner?

15. What color would you suggest using on the cover of a catalog advertising a boys' camp?

16. List the colors you consider to be very good background colors.

17. When using red as a background color would it be better to print black type on the red background or reverse the type? (White letter with red background.)

18. Why should yellow type not be used on white paper?

19. Why would a tint of violet not be a good color to use on an advertisement for men's suits?

ONE COLOR AND BLACK (FIFTY COLOR)

...pe and paper influence the selection of color on the printed page. Color ...ny is an aid to beauty; it should invite reading and make the entire layout ...e harmonious and appealing. ...lor is not intelligently applied, money spent on it might better be saved.

If color is not used correctly it will attract more attention than the type (Fig. 1), when it should do just the opposite. Notice how the colored rules in Fig. 1 are so dark they attract the reader's attention from the type.

A large percentage of printing makes use of black type on white paper. When a color is to be used with the type and paper, the weight of the color should be considered. If the color is used by the printer just as it comes in the ink can, there is a chance that it will stand out more than the type as in Fig. 1.

The value or weight of the color should always be considered. For example, speaking of weight, black may be considered as "100" because of its solidness. White stock, because of its brightness, lacks weight and may be considered "O" (Fig. 2). Therefore, a proper color balance in printing can be obtained if the color, the third element, is given a weight that lies midway between the black and white, that is, at a "fifty" level (Fig. 3). When using the "fifty" color with black type on white paper, the black type will stand out more than the color and will be easily read (Fig. 4).

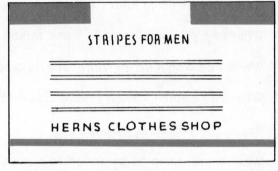

Fig. 1

Color is too dark. It stands out as much as black. See Fig. 1

A "fifty" color

Fig. 2   Fig. 3

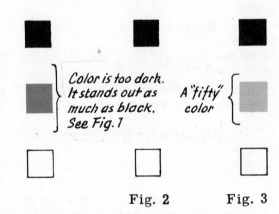

Fig. 4

154

On the color wheel the darkest color is violet and the lightest is yellow. Therefore, black would be located just below violet and white above yellow on the wheel (Fig. 5). If black were gradually added to white, a grey ink would be formed, becoming darker as more black is added. A graduation from white to black could be formed as in the center of the color wheel (Fig. 5). In the center of the wheel halfway between black and white is a grey that is of "fifty" value. When selecting a grey to use with black type on white paper, this "fifty" grey should be used.

When using one color with black on white paper, all colors below the center of the wheel are too dark and should be mixed with white in order to bring them up to the "fifty" level. The colors above the center of the wheel are not too dark, but in some cases may be too light and weak. In such cases they should be darkened by adding black ink, or by adding the color that is opposite on the color wheel. For example, orange could be mixed to a "fifty" value by the addition of black or the opposite color, blue.

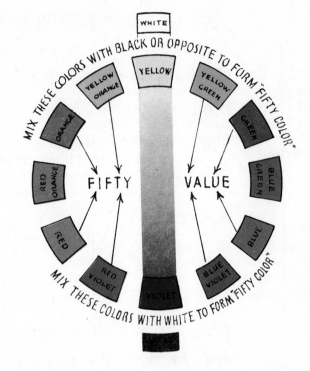

Fig. 5

COLOR WORK

COLOR **WORK**

Fig. 6

RULES AND TYPE IN COLOR

When using a "fifty" color, the weight of the type or a rule should be increased. As the "fifty" color is one half the weight of black, a word in color will have to be set in a bolder face than words in black in order to have them stand out as much as the black letters (Fig. 6).

A black rule underscoring a word should always be the same thickness as the stroke of the type. If the rule is to be printed in a "fifty" color, it will have to be twice as thick to harmonize with the type, as the color is one half as dark in tone (Fig. 7).

COLOR IN PRINTING

COLOR IN PRINTING

Fig. 7

```
┌──────────────── THE LAYOUT ────────────────┐
│                    COPY (A)                  │
│                                              │
│  SIZE:  6 in. by 3 3/4 in. deep              │
│                                              │
│  DISPLAY HEAD:  Booth does good Printing     │
│                                              │
│  BODY:  Governed by a principle so simple and sincere as to seem,│
│         in these days of intemperate claim and inordinate promise,│
│         all but unimpressive: "To give the best service possible."│
│         Upon this basis, we solicit your printing orders.│
│                                              │
│  SIGNATURE:  O. E. Booth Printing Service    │
│              907 Clinton Avenue              │
│              Des Moines, Iowa                │
│                                              │
│                    COPY (B)                  │
│                                              │
│  SIZE:  6 in. by 3 3/4 in. deep              │
│                                              │
│  DISPLAY HEAD:  Colgate Football Schedule    │
│                                              │
│  COPY:  October  5  Temple at Colgate        │
│         October 12  LaFayette at Colgate     │
│         October 19  West Point at West Point │
│         October 26  Brown at Providence      │
│         November  2  Holy Cross at Colgate   │
│         November  9  Tulane at New York      │
│         November 23  Syracuse at Syracuse    │
│         November 30  Columbia at New York    │
│                                              │
│  SIGNATURE:  Columbia Printing Company       │
│              622 Bleeker Street              │
│              New York, New York              │
└──────────────────────────────────────────────┘
```

DIRECTIONS

1. Arrange one of the above blotters.

2. You may use color, tint blocks or rules.

Unit 57   COLOR COMBINATIONS

Instead of using one color with black, the printing designer at times may wish to combine two or more colors. It has been found that combinations of certain colors do not appear pleasing to a reader's eye. Therefore, it is necessary for the layout man and printer to know how to select colors that appear harmonious when used together.

MONOCHROMATIC HARMONIES

A monochromatic color harmony is secured by using two or more tones of one color. When used correctly on a printed piece, the tints and shades of a color are appealing. When printing on colored paper, the designer is always certain to secure a pleasing effect if the color used on the printed piece is a shade of the colored stock. For example, a deep blue type on a pale blue stock, deep green type on a pale green stock, deep purple on pale lavender and so on offer good harmonies.

On white stock a monochromatic harmony may be secured by using dark colored type with tint blocks, rules and so forth in a lighter tone (Fig. 1). When using this combination, the designer should make certain that the type is the darkest in tone, with the tone of the ornaments one half as dark as the type and the stock lightest.

ANALOGOUS COLOR HARMONY

Another method of securing color harmony is to combine adjacent (next to each other) colors of the printer's color wheel, such as blue and violet, red and orange, and similar combinations (Fig. 2). These colors harmonize, as each pair is related. For example, red and orange are very closely related, as orange is formed by combining red and yellow and, containing a small amount of red, should harmonize with red.

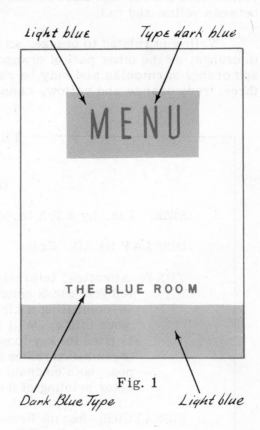

Fig. 1

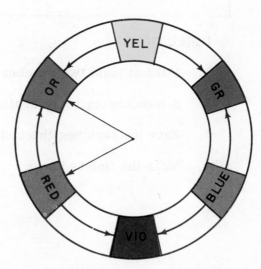

Fig. 2 *Method of selecting analogous color harmonies*

Only adjacent colors that are closely related should be combined. For instance, yellow used with orange and red will not harmonize because there is no relationship between yellow and red.

Yellow is related to orange, as a part of orange is yellow. Red is also related to orange, as the other part of orange is red. Therefore, red and orange or yellow and orange harmonize and may be used on the same jobs, but a combination of all three, red, orange and yellow, cannot be used harmoniously together.

THE LAYOUT

BLOTTER

SIZE: 7 in. by 3 1/2 in. deep

DISPLAY HEAD: Color

TEXT: Attention, interest, buying appeal and beauty...the intelligent use of color combines all of these. Your printing is combating a highly competitive field when it leaves your office. Will it hold its own or will it fail? Color is often the key to successful printed matter. The Ingrim organization makes a specialty of color work and is equipped, both mechanically and in its personnel, to produce color printing of the greatest utility and beauty.

SIGNATURE: Ingrim Printing Company
18 Canal Street
New York, New York

DIRECTIONS

1. Make at least two thumbnail sketches of the blotter copy.

2. A monochromatic or analogous color harmony must be used.

3. Have the sketches checked by the instructor.

4. Make the finished layout.

Unit 58   COMPLEMENTARY COLOR HARMONIES

COMPLEMENTS

Besides using the monochromatic and analogous methods of harmonizing colors, a printing designer may form pleasing color combinations by using colors together that are directly opposite each other on the color wheel (Fig. 1).   This is known as the complementary method.   The color schemes formed by using the analogous and monochromatic methods of selecting colors tend to be soft and refined.   This is not true of complementary harmonies, as they form contrasts that attract attention.

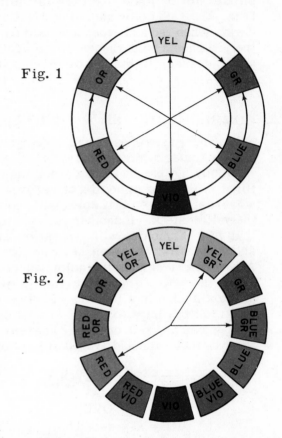

Fig. 1

Fig. 2

On the printer's color wheel, the commonly known colors that are opposite each other and form a complementary harmony are as follows: yellow and violet, red and green, blue and orange.   These combinations consist of a warm color and a cool one that offer a good contrast and can be used together wherever a color harmony is wanted that will be outstanding.

Red and green are perhaps the two most spectacular.   Red is an advancing color while green is cool and fresh.   Used together they attract attention.   The combination of blue and orange has been called the most beautiful in existence.   The orange is warm, friendly and a glowing color, quite the opposite of blue which is cold.   The combination is very pleasing.   They look best when a small amount of orange is used with a large amount of blue.

Yellow and violet produce a combination that is a little more refined.   Yellow is a very bright color, while violet is retiring and dignified.   Many pleasing effects can be secured by using these two colors together.

Besides the above mentioned combinations there are other complementary harmonies, such as red-violet and yellow-green, yellow-orange and blue-violet, red-orange and blue-green.

SPLIT COMPLEMENTS

The colors on each side of the complement on the color wheel may be used instead of the complementary color.   For instance, instead of using red and green, the colors on each side of these two colors on the color wheel may be used. In this case the color combination would be red, blue-green and yellow-green (Fig. 2). This is called a split-complement and when desired may be applied to any opposite combination on the color wheel.

USE OF COMPLEMENTS

When using two complementary colors, they should not be used together in their pure form (Fig. 3). One color should be light and the other dark. When red and green are used on white stock, the red should be darkened by the addition of black and the green lightened by mixing it with white (Fig. 4).

COMPLEMENTS AND A THIRD COLOR

There are times when the designer of printing wishes to use a third color with a complementary harmony. A bright yellow stock may be selected for a job. The opposite of yellow on the color wheel is violet, so that color will look pleasing on the yellow stock. If another color is to be selected that will harmonize with the yellow and violet, it should be halfway between the two colors in strength. A line drawn across the color wheel halfway between the yellow and violet (Line A-B Fig. 5) and at right angles to a line drawn between the yellow and violet (Line C-D Fig. 5) will pass through blue-green and red-orange. Therefore, either of these two colors should be used with yellow and violet.

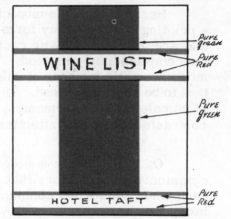

Fig. 3

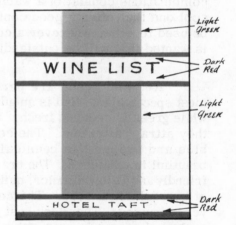

Fig. 4

THE LAYOUT

COVER

SIZE: 4 in. by 6 in. deep

COPY: Would **YOU** believe this?

DIRECTIONS

1. Make two thumbnail sketches of the cover, using a complementary harmony of colors.

2. Black may be used with the colors if desired.

3. Have the instructor check the sketches and aid in selecting the better one.

4. Make the finished layout, using colored pencils to apply the color.

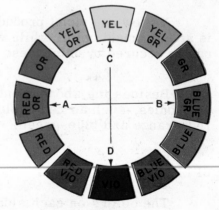

Fig. 5

Unit 59   TRIAD COLOR HARMONY

Besides the monochromatic, analogous and complementary methods of harmonizing colors have been explained, there is a fourth method known as the <u>triad</u>.   This is called the triad method because it consists of three colors that harmonize.

TRIAD METHOD

Triad combinations are found on the color wheel by taking a triangle that points to the three colors red, yellow and blue and then swinging it around to any three colors on the wheel. For example, the primary triad is red, yellow and blue (Fig. 1). If the triangle is shifted so that one angle points at orange, then the other two will point at green and violet (Fig. 2). This combination is more refined than the first and would be better on a more dignified type of job than the red, yellow and blue. Another triad combination is the green-yellow, violet-blue and red-orange (Fig. 3). The most beautiful triad of all consists of yellow-orange, blue-green and red-violet (Fig. 4). Each of these colors is beautiful, and the combination is very pleasing.

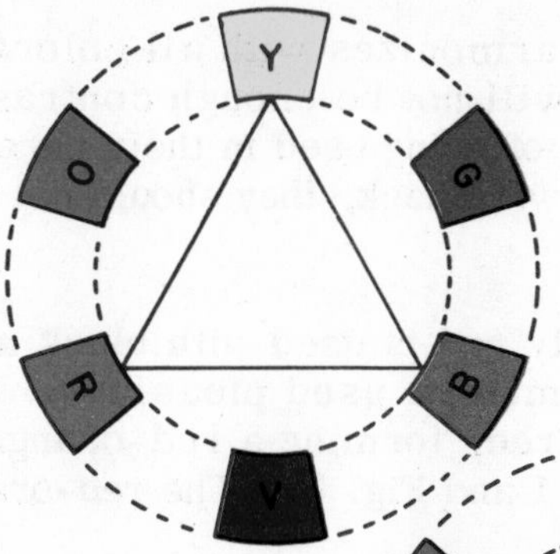

Fig. 1

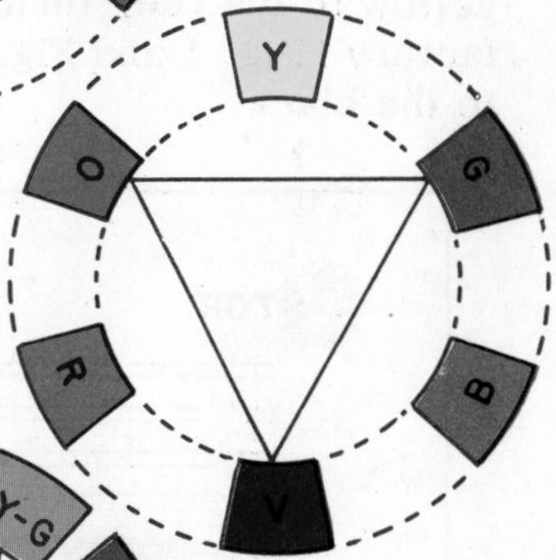

Fig. 2

Fig. 3

Fig. 4

USING THE TRIAD HARMONY

When using three colors as triad combinations, they should not all be the same intensity or strength. One should be light in tone, one dark and the other halfway between the two in strength. Equal amounts of the colors should not be used, but a large amount of one and smaller amounts of the other two will give harmonious results.

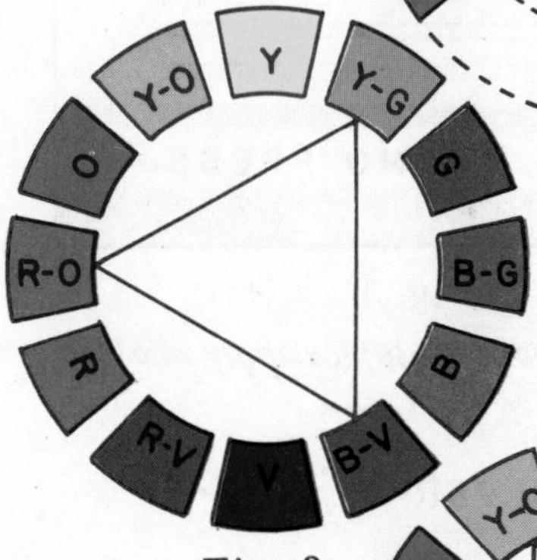

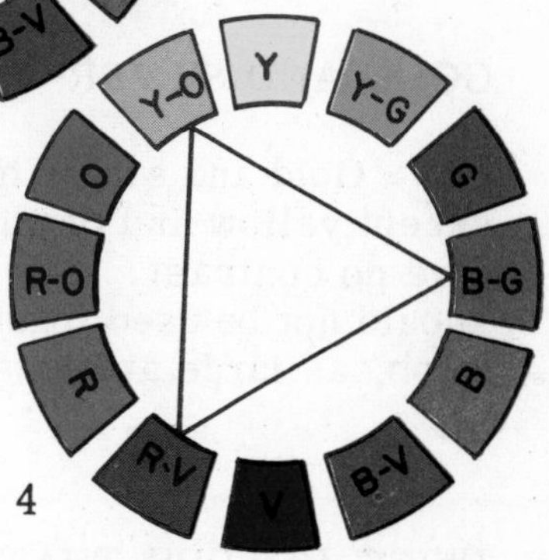

```
┌───────  THE  LAYOUT  ───────┐
│                             │
│  SIZE:  4 in. by 5 in. deep │
│                             │
│  COPY:  Toys and Games      │
│         Children's Toy Co.  │
│                             │
└─────────────────────────────┘
```

DIRECTIONS

1. Arrange the cover, having the instructor check the sketches before making the finished layout.
2. A triad color harmony must be used.
3. Have the instructor check the finished layout.

Unit 60   BLACK, WHITE AND GRAY

Black, white and gray are not colors but they may be used with any color or combination of colors and result in perfect harmony.

Black harmonizes with all colors, but if used with cool colors (blue, green, violet) there will not be enough contrast to brighten the page unless the colors are tints, instead of being used in their pure form. If warm colors (orange and yellow) are to be used with black, they should not be tints but should be used in their full value.

Probably red is used with black more than any other single color. At times a pure red ink may be used pleasingly with black, but in most cases the addition of yellow to the red, forming a red-orange, will give a color that is much more satisfactory (Fig. 1 and Fig. 2). The red-orange is brighter and forms a stronger contrast to the black.

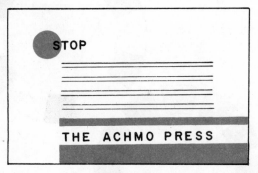

Fig. 1

Pure red is too dark to use pleasingly with black.

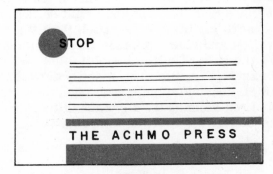

Fig. 2

Red-orange is lighter and forms a pleasing contrast.

GOLD AND SILVER

Gold and silver harmonize with all colors. Gold may be used with all colors except yellow and orange which, because they are the same in appearance and tone, give no contrast. Silver and gray, being similar, do not form a contrast and so should not be used together. Only small amounts of gold or silver should be used on a job, as large amounts of these metallic colors give an unpleasant effect.

USING COLORS THAT DO NOT HARMONIZE

Colors that do not harmonize may be brought into harmony by separating them with bands or edgings of black, white, gray, gold or silver. Red and blue are used together frequently and are not considered a harmonious combination of colors. Yet, by separating the blue and red with a band of white, black, gray or gold, they will not clash but will appear pleasing to the eye.

COLOR BALANCE

Color, like type used on a printed page, should be balanced. If color is used above the optical center, it should be balanced by color below the center. If color is used on one side of a page, as on a letterhead, it should be repeated on the other side. The larger the mass of color the nearer the center of the page it should be placed.

MIXING COLORED INKS

When mixing colors, the lighter color should be placed on the slab first and the darker color added to it. Mixing inks in this manner will save time and money. In making a tint of blue, for example, if the white were added to the blue, too large a quantity of ink might be mixed before the desired tint was achieved. Black, however, should be added to the color instead of the color to the black.

THE LAYOUT

ANNOUNCEMENT

SIZE: 4 in. by 6 in. deep

DISPLAY HEAD: Announcing a New Department

TEXT: The Cunard Press takes pleasure in announcing that Mr.
Otto C. Fields has been appointed as director of our new
Department of Layout and Design.

SIGNATURE: The Cunard Press
1010 Broadway
New York, New York

DIRECTIONS

1. Make two thumbnail sketches of the announcement.

2. One color and black may be used.

3. Have the sketches checked by the instructor.

4. Make the finished layout.

5. Mark the layout for the compositor.

Unit 61   DIVISION OF SPACE

A great many printed pieces, especially covers, are arranged so that a part of a page is one color while another section of the page is another color, or the color of the paper. When color is not employed, there are times when a designer desires to have a section of the page solid black or gray, and the remaining area white, or the color of the paper. In order to arrange pages and areas into two tones, it is necessary for the designer to have a knowledge of interesting space divisions.

A page might be arranged with the space broken equally (Fig. 1) and a cover created from this division (Fig. 2). This cover would undoubtedly be satisfactory, but if the space were broken unevenly (Fig. 3) the cover would be more interesting (Fig. 4).

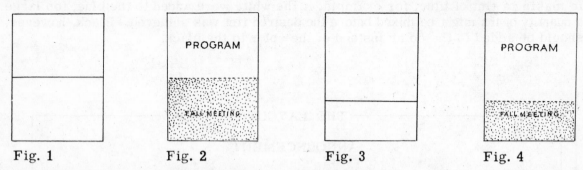

Fig. 1   Fig. 2   Fig. 3   Fig. 4

By drawing vertical and horizontal straight lines, off center, numerous unequal divisions may be created. For example, two lines may be sketched as in Fig. 5. These lines form unequal divisions so that when the areas are darkened, each space is a different size and shape. The unequal divisions should in every case form a very interesting cover (Fig. 6).

Besides using straight lines to divide space, ovals, circles, triangles and other geometric shapes may be employed (Fig. 7, 8, 9).

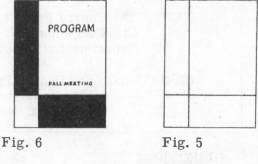

Fig. 6   Fig. 5

Fig. 7   Fig. 8   Fig. 9

In every case the copy should always be studied before the space is broken, in order to form an appropriate arrangement. The arrangement used for the cover in Fig. 10 is not appropriate, as the arrangement does not harmonize with the name of the restaurant. The triangular arrangement in Fig. 11 is much more appropriate.

Fig. 10

Fig. 11

THE LAYOUT

COVER (A)

SIZE: 4 in. by 6 in. deep

COPY: Exhibition of Modern Furniture
Bender Studios
Fifth Avenue, New York

COVER (B)

SIZE: 4 in. by 6 in.

COPY: Plumbing for the Home
Hart and Co.
New York, New York

DIRECTIONS

1. Select either copy (A) or copy (B) and make at least two thumbnail sketches.

2. One or more colors may be used.

3. Have the instructor check the sketches and then make the finished layout.

Unit 62   WINDOW CARDS AND POSTERS

Window cards, sometimes called show cards, are usually placed in store windows to advertise some of the store's merchandise or local dances, shows, exhibits and similar occasions. The sizes of window cards are regulated by the size of the large sheets from which they are cut. The large sheet, called a full sheet is purchased in the size 22" by 28". A half sheet is 14" by 22", and 11" by 14" is the size of the quarter sheet. Some cards are also made in the size 28" by 44" which is called a double sheet. It is a good policy for a printing designer to become familiar with these sizes, as it is a common practice for a customer to order a half sheet or quarter sheet card. Besides the sizes already mentioned, other sizes are sometimes used, as the cards might be cut from cover stock or some other paper which would undoubtedly come in another size.

POSTERS

Posters are usually larger than window cards and are displayed outside on poster boards, fences and buildings. The sizes of posters vary and are standardized only when they are to be posted on the posterboards. For example, a large poster is 8'-8" by 9'-6" and is commonly called a 24-sheet poster. Another standard size is the three-sheet board which takes a poster 42" by 84".

DESIGNING WINDOW CARDS AND POSTERS

As window cards and posters are read from a distance, the type employed should be larger and bolder than that used on printing that is to be held in the reader's hands. Do not set every line in a large size type (Fig. 1), as it would be difficult for the reader who glances at the printed piece to get the message. It would be much more effective to select the one or two outstanding points in the advertisement, setting them in the largest size type, keeping the rest of the type lines smaller in size, but not so small that they cannot be read at a reasonable distance (Fig. 2).

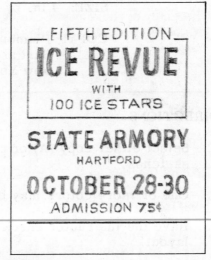

Fig. 1   Fig. 2

It is necessary to select plain, simple types that are very easy to read at a distance, and if more than one family of type is employed, to select types that harmonize.

The copy used on window cards should be as brief as possible, giving only the necessary information. The layout man should select the lines that will convey the message to the person who only glances at the printed piece, and display them larger than the others. The most important line or unit should be placed in the focal point, just above the center (Fig. 2). The longest lines and the darkest areas should also be placed above the center if possible so that the greatest amount of weight would be massed there.

Besides the poster or window card, there are other objects on the street and in windows to attract the eye. Therefore, the poster or card should be arranged to draw attention. Color undoubtedly is used more than any thing else to attract the eye. When using color, it might be well to recall that the warm colors are advancing and will attract more attention than others. The cool colors form very good backgrounds. For distance reading yellow and black form the best combination, while green on white is the second choice. Complementary harmonies, it has been found, attract more attention than the analogous, triad or monochromatic. Above all, when using color, it should be remembered that the color should not attract more attention than the type, as the type carries the important message.

Fig. 3

Off center arrangements can be used as well as boxes with shadow rules (Fig. 3).

At times a card or poster that is easily read at close range cannot be read quickly by persons some distance away. Therefore, before printing, it is always safest to test the layout from a distance making certain it attracts attention and is easy to read.

THE LAYOUT

WINDOW CARD (A)

SIZE: Quarter sheet
COPY: Third Annual Auto Show
State Armory
Week of October 5th
Admission Free

DIRECTIONS

1. Make two thumbnail sketches of Copy (A).

2. One or more colors may be used.

3. Have the sketches checked by the instructor.

4. Make the finished layout.

SECTION IV   REVIEW

1. Name the following: (a) primary colors (b) secondary colors (c) intermediate colors.

2. If green ink were added to white ink would the combination form a shade of green or a tint of green?

3. (a) Which of the pure colors do the largest percentage of men prefer above all other colors?

    (b) What color appeals to women above all other colors?

4. What is the best color selection to use with either black or white on a poster that is to be read at a distance?

5. Name at least three colors that would make good background colors for type printed in black.

6. Make a sketch of the printer's color wheel, showing the position of the various colors in their proper order.

7. If a person mentioned that a "fifty" color should be used on the job, what would he mean?

8. Why should a rule that underscores a word be twice as thick as the stroke of the type when it is printed in a "fifty" color?

9. Explain the difference between a monochromatic color harmony and an analogous (adjacent) color harmony.

10. What color would you select if you were to print on a light blue stock?

11. Name three complementary color harmonies.

12. Explain the difference between a complementary harmony and a split complementary harmony.

13. For a piece of printing to attract attention would it be better to select a complementary harmony or a monochromatic harmony of colors?

14. If violet ink were being used on yellow paper and a third color were to be selected to use for a border, what color would you select to use with the yellow and violet? Explain how the selection was made.

15. A job is to be printed in three colors. Suggest three colors that will harmonize.

16. If a job to be printed contained two colors that did not harmonize, what one thing could be done by the designer to make the colors look pleasing together?

Special Layout Considerations

Unit 63   SCALING PHOTOGRAPHS AND ART WORK

The layout man or printer, before arranging a printing job, often has to scale a photograph or art work.   Nearly all art work is drawn larger than the size it is to be printed in, and often photographs have to be reduced.   Before a layout can be started the designer must know the exact dimensions the art work and photographs are to be in the printed job.

There are several mechanical scales and slide rules that may be used to figure the dimensions in scaling copy.   If they are not available it is possible for the reduction to be figured mathematically, or by the use of the diagonal line method.

DIAGONAL LINE METHOD

A piece of art work measuring 3 in. wide by 4 in. deep·is to be reduced to a width of 3/4 in. In order to find the depth, place a piece of tracing paper over the art work and draw the outside lines that measure 3 in. by 4 in. Draw a diagonal line lightly from the upper right hand corner, A to the lower left hand corner, B. From B measure 3/4 in., the width the cut is to be made, placing a mark at D. From the 3/4 in. mark, D, draw a line at right angle to the line, B--C, and extend it until it intersects the diagonal line at E. The length of the line, D--E, will be the depth of the cut or 1 in. The space that this art work would occupy when reduced would be 3/4 in. by 1 in.

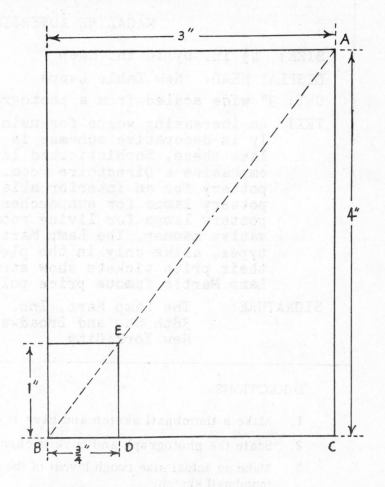

MATHEMATICAL METHOD

It is possible to scale artwork and photographs by the use of ratio and proportion since the copy width and depth reduce or enlarge in exact proportion to the length of the diagonal.

WIDTH OF PHOTO : DEPTH OF PHOTO :: WIDTH OF CUT : X

3 in. : 4 in. : : 3/4 in. : x

Multiply the extremes: . 3 in. times x equals 3x
Multiply the means: 4 in. times 3/4 in. equals 3

Therefore 3x equals 3

x equals $\frac{3}{3}$

x equals 1 inch (depth of the cut)

THE LAYOUT

MAGAZINE ADVERTISEMENT

SIZE: $4\frac{1}{2}$ in. by 10 in. deep

DISPLAY HEAD: New Table Lamps

CUT: 3" wide scaled from a photograph $4\frac{1}{2}$" by 6" deep.

TEXT: An increasing vogue for using table lamps lavish-
ly in decorative schemes is responsible for lamps
like these. Sophisticated little French lamps to
emphasize a Directoire room. Sleek modern ones in
pottery for an interior a la Ruhlmann. Gay Italian
pottery lamps for sunporches. Unusual Chinese
pottery lamps for living rooms in a rich, conservative manner. The Lamp Mart offers lamps of many
types, alike only in the pleasant detail that
their price tickets show striking evidence of The
Lamp Mart's famous price policy.

SIGNATURE: The Lamp Mart, Inc.
38th St. and Broadway
New York City

DIRECTIONS

1. Make a thumbnail sketch and have it checked by the instructor.

2. Scale the photograph and have it checked by the instructor.

3. Make an actual size rough layout of the advertisement following the thumbnail sketch.

4. Copyfit the text, selecting the type and type size you believe to be appropriate. Have the work checked.

5. Make the finished layout.

Unit 64   COPY PREPARATION FOR PHOTO-ENGRAVING

Time and money are wasted by many layout men and printers who handle and mark photo-engraving copy incorrectly. If the following suggestions are remembered and applied, much time will be saved, costly delays and "make-overs" avoided.

MARKING COPY FOR PHOTO-ENGRAVING

When marking dimensions on photographs or drawings for the engraver, it is necessary to mark only one dimension, (Fig. 1). It is common practice to write the dimension in blue pencil as light blue will not ordinarily photograph. Dimensions may be written on the edge of photographs or art work, (Fig. 1).

WRITING ON PHOTOGRAPHS

Instructions should not be written on the back of a photograph. The writing may indent the surface, forming a shadow that will appear on the finished engraving. Instructions may be written on the edge of art work with a blue pencil, but should be written on a separate slip of paper and attached to photographs, (Fig. 2).

ATTACHING INSTRUCTIONS

Instructions written on a separate slip of paper should be tipped on the margin of the photograph, and never clipped on with a paper clip. The clip often cracks the photograph and these cracks are apt to appear on the finished plate.

ROLLING PHOTOGRAPHS

A large photograph that must be rolled before going to the engraver should be rolled with the face of the picture on the outside. If the gelantinized surface should crack from the rolling, the cracks may close up when the photograph is flattened out. Never roll a photograph unless it is necessary.

Fig. 1

Fig. 2

CROPPING AND CROP MARKS

When a part of a photograph is to be "cut out" so that it will not appear in the engraving, the graphic arts term applied to this operation is "cropped". When a photograph is to be cropped it must be marked so that the engraver will know what to eliminate or crop.

Crop marks should be placed in the margin of the photograph as in Fig. 3. If it is necessary to draw lines on the photograph, a china marking pencil should be used. These lines may be removed with a damp cloth without damaging the photograph.

Fig. 3

THE LAYOUT

MAILING CARD

SIZE: 5½" x 3½" deep.

DISPLAY HEAD: Type

TEXT: Printing is roughly 500 years old. The basis of it is movable type. The past 25 years have seen a tremendous outpouring of type designs, which few other quarter centuries could equal in number. You will find the best advertising type designs of all available to you here.

SIGNATURE: Bard Typographers, Inc.
New York, Chicago, Boston

DIRECTIONS

1. Make a thumbnail sketch of the layout.
2. One color and black may be used.
3. Make the finished layout indicating the color on the layout with a colored pencil.
4. Have the instructor check the finished layout.

Unit 65   MARKING COPY FOR THE COMPOSITOR

One of the purposes of the layout is to save time in the composing room. If it is to save time, it must provide the compositor with all the information concerning the job.

First, the width and depth of the page or advertisement should be given. In commercial work it is usually given in picas, but in newspapers it is given in column widths and inches, or agate lines. These measurements should be written in the upper left corner of the layout (Fig. 1).

In magazine work the page is considered the unit of measure for large advertisements. Space is designated as full page, half-page, quarter page, etc. Very small advertisements are marked according to the number of agate lines in depth.

The first measurement given in newspapers selling their space by the column inch is always the width such as 2 by 8 which means 2 columns wide by 8 inches deep. In newspapers selling their space by the agate line, the depth is sometimes given first such as 140 by 4 which means 140 agate lines deep by 4 columns wide.

All display lines should be lettered and marked. The lettering should be similar to the type used. The width or measure of the line and the size and name of the type face should be indicated for all type lines. The measure, point size, and face should be given for the body type. The text should always be copyfitted so that it will set, as marked, in the space allowed in the layout.

Fig. 1

When marking copy, the measure should be given first, then the point size and name of the type...thus: set 20 picas, 18 point garamond caps and lower case. This is usually shortened to 20/18 gar. c and l.c. If the type is to be leaded the amount of leading should be indicated. When a smaller size type is to be set on a larger body it should be indicated...thus: 10 on 12 gar. which would mean that 10 point garamond would be set on a 12 point body.

Some shops have an alphabetical system of designating their type. A certain letter following the type size indicates a certain type face. Other shops designate type by numerals instead of letters.

If the layout contains rules, cuts, initials, etc., they should be clearly marked so that the sizes and dimensions will be understood by the compositor and make-up men.

In book and commercial work the margin dimensions and size of stock should be clearly indicated.

In most commercial plants and newspaper composing rooms, it is preferred to have the typewritten copy marked, as well as the layout. As most composition is set by machine, the operator does not wish to have a large layout before him at the machine. If the copy is marked on the typewritten sheet giving the measure and size of type, he will be able to proceed without the layout. The copy should be marked with the directions on the left side of each typewritten display line or group of text matter.

```
──────── THE LAYOUT ────────
        MAGAZINE ADVERTISEMENT

SIZE:  3½" x 10"
DISPLAY HEAD:  A Cooling Treatment
CUT:  Girl's head 3" wide scaled from photo 4¼" x 5".
CUT:  Cosmetics 1 3/4" wide scaled from photo 3½" x 4".
TEXT: Jane Moore has a cool and beautifying treatment
      for days when the mercury runs riot. Pour Ledina
      Skin Tonic into a small bowl of cracked ice . .
      moisten a cotton pad in its chilled depths,dip in-
      to your jar of Ledina Cleansing Cream and cleanse
      with an upward motion. After every trace of this
      refreshing mixture is removed, pat with iced skin
      tonic until your skin and spirits are radiant.
SIGNATURE:  Jane Moore Salon  -   Fifth Avenue, New York
```

DIRECTIONS
1. Make a thumbnail sketch of the magazine advertisement and have the instructor check it.
2. Copyfit the text and make the finished layout.
3. Mark the complete advertisement for the compositor with a colored pencil, (preferably blue).

Unit 66   CREATING SHAPE IN LAYOUT

Too little attention is given in most cases, to the shape of a layout. By shape is meant the outline formed by the outside edges of the layout. The mass effect of the layout produces a definite shape or form that should not be overlooked.

Interesting, unfamiliar shapes (Fig. 1) will tend to hold a persons attention and interest longer than a familiar, ordinary shape such as a rectangle, (Fig. 2).

A layout might be arranged so that the type and cuts form a squared effect, touching the top, sides, and bottom repeatedly (Fig. 3). The result is the forming of an uninteresting ordinary shape, eliminating practically all white space. The same copy could be arranged so that the layout shape would be interesting and pleasing, (Fig. 4), holding the reader's attention longer.

THE FOUR POINT METHOD

There are various methods of arranging a layout so that an interesting shape is created. One of the most popular is the four point method.

When using the four point method the top, sides and bottom of the type page are touched once and only once, (Fig. 5). If an illustration touches the top measure, no other part should do so. If the display head touches both sides, the other parts should be kept narrower. If the signature touches the bottom of the type page, no other part should be allowed to go so low.

The four point method can be applied to practically any type of printing layout. It should not be used in every case, as there are times when a squared arrangement should be used to give a piece of printing a dignified, conservative appearance.

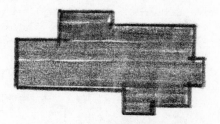
Fig. 1 *Interesting shape. Would tend to attract attention and create interest*

Fig. 2 *Familiar, ordinary shape*

Fig. 3 *Layout forms ordinary uninteresting shape*

Fig. 4 *Layout forms unusual, interesting shape.*

New

magnificent! FROM PARIS

THE *Mode* SHOP

Fig. 5 *Note the four points touching the type page sides, once and only once*

THE LAYOUT

MAGAZINE ADVERTISEMENT

SIZE: 7 in. by 10 in. deep

DISPLAY HEAD: Announcing a New Chrysler

CUT: 3 in. by 4 in. deep

TEXT: The copy is to be written after the layout has been completed, so no definite amount of space has to be reserved for the text.

SIGNATURE: CHRYSLER "270"

DIRECTIONS

1. Make a thumbnail sketch and have it checked by the instructor.

2. Make the finished layout, using the four point method.

3. Select text type and figure the number of words that would have to be written to fill the space allowed for text in the layout.

4. Mark the layout for the compositor with a colored pencil.

Unit 67   NEWSPAPER LAYOUTS

All the basic principles of layout apply to advertisements designed for newspapers, but a number of factors peculiar to newspaper layout deserve special consideration.

The layout man must realize that a newspaper advertisement, unless very large, will undoubtedly appear with other advertisements. Because of this, the advertisement will have competition in securing the reader's attention and holding his interest, (Fig. 1).

It is necessary that the layout man consider these points concerning competing interests and provide means for overcoming them. The other advertisements may be larger or smaller in size, stronger or weaker in contrast value, and each wages its separate battle for the reader's attention. The layout man has no way of knowing beforehand whether his layout may be surrounded by other advertisements featuring machines, clothing, furniture or shoes. He must realize this and arrange his layout so that it will be sure to stand out alone when placed among the others, (Fig. 2).

There are several methods of separating advertisements. One of the most common is the use of a rule around the entire layout, (Fig. 3).

As the reader turns the pages of a newspaper the advertisement should catch the eye in some manner. The display lines should be set large enough or bold enough to quickly carry the message to the reader, at once, with what is being offered, and where it can be purchased, (Fig. 3).

The advertisement should not be over displayed. If several heads are set large, they will compete with each other and nothing will be emphasized. The feature or statement which is most desirable to bring to the notice of the reader should be accented. Other features or sales arguments should be placed in the body.

Fig. 1 *Because of similar layout styles, the two advertisements run together and appear to be one adv.*

Fig. 2 *Two advertisements that separate very well*

Every available device for the promotion of easy reading should be used in the planning of newspaper layouts. Today we read in a hurry, or do not read at all. Advertisements that slow down our reading speed will not get results. This means that types used should be as large in point size as space permits.

Type should not be set too wide. Nothing discourages the reader so much as lines of type so long that the eye cannot follow back and pick up the beginning of the next line with ease and certainty. It is wise to break up long lines into columns.

Adequate leading between lines is also necessary, particularly when using modern types. Display lines set in caps and lower case are much easier to read than all caps.

Illustrations and large display lines are used to attract attention in newspaper advertisements, but the use of white space is also one of the best methods of attracting attention.

It should be remembered that the printing results in newspapers differ from commercial printing. Because of the poorer quality of paper and ink, and the speed of the presses, the layout man is required to use coarse screen halftones which fail to reproduce as fine detail as the fine screen engravings.

Many layout men prefer to use line engravings with Ben Day in order to secure sharper illustrations. Thin line types, because of the stereotyping process, tend to thicken and are not as satisfactory as types with wide strokes. Solid blacks usually appear as dark greys when printed, and sometimes greys appear darker than planned.

Fig. 3 *Separated by the use of rules*

The layout man therefore, must plan newspaper layouts realizing that his advertisement must be separated from the others; it must be arranged so the message can be read at a glance; and, he must consider several mechanical limitations.

┌─────────────────── THE LAYOUT ───────────────────┐

COPY (A) NEWSPAPER ADVERTISEMENT

SIZE: 2 columns (24 picas) by 8½" deep.

DISPLAY HEAD: Summer Dresses

TEXT: They look so decorative...these handmade summer dresses in linens and cotton laces. Designed for us by a famous creator of gowns, and presented to you at very special prices.

SUBHEAD: While they last $16.75

CUT: A cut of a girl in a summer dress (Any size desired)

SIGNATURE: Dressland Inc.
            On the Avenue

COPY (B) NEWSPAPER ADVERTISEMENT

SIZE: 2 columns (24 picas) by 9" deep.

DISPLAY HEAD: Red, White and Blue Shoes

CUT: A cut of slippers any size desired.

TEXT: The Shoe Box salutes the Summer, and the Fourth, with a flag series of shoes in red and white, and in blue and white. The chic buckle opera, in linen, open to the breeze at heel and toe. Below, the famous anklet Bandanna, in crepe. Nearly a dozen other equally gay models ready to declare a holiday of color for your feet.

SIGNATURE: The Shoe Box
            5th Avenue at 58th St.

└───┘

DIRECTIONS

1. Select either copy (A) or copy (B) and make a thumbnail sketch.

2. Have the sketch checked by the instructor.

3. Make the finished layout, marking it for the compositor with a colored pencil.

Unit 68   METHODS OF SEPARATING NEWSPAPER ADVERTISEMENTS

There are several methods of separating newspaper advertisements. The most common is the use of a black rule around the entire advertisement. This will box in the advertisement, and thus separate it (Fig. 1).

Various combinations of rules may be used as well as hand drawn or decorative borders, (Fig. 2).

Fig. 1

Fig. 2

Rules may be used on two sides as in Fig. 3. In this case the rules will separate the advertisement from the displays that are on each side, but another method, such as white space, must be used to take care of the top and the bottom. Quite often the rules are used at the head and foot of the advertisement and white space at the sides.

A box may be used around a part of an advertisement, (Fig. 4), letting white space separate the other sections of the advertisement.

Fig. 3

Fig. 4

White space is a great asset to an advertisement as it will attract attention on a grey page of type. At times white space is used around the entire advertisement as a method of separating it from the other displays.

One method employed to surround the advertisement with white space is the four point method. Each side of the type area is touched once and only once, by cuts, type or rules, when this method is employed (Fig. 5).

Fig. 5

At times reverse engravings are used as in Fig. 6. This is a method that at times fails to separate the advertisement. The bottom of the advertisement placed above it might also be reversed, and this would tend to make the two appear as one.

Besides the methods described, there are several others which a layout man may safely use. It is very important that some method of separating the advertisements be used in newspaper layout.

Fig. 6

THE LAYOUT

NEWSPAPER ADVERTISEMENT

SIZE: 3 columns by 48 picas deep

DISPLAY HEAD: Welcome to Nova Scotia

CUT: 24 picas wide scaled from a photograph 6 in. by 4 3/4 in.

SUB-HEAD: Tours $125 and up

TEXT: Reserve the amount of space you desire for the text.

SIGNATURE: Eastern Steamship Lines

DIRECTIONS

1. Make a thumbnail sketch of the above copy using a method of separating the advertisement other than a rule around the entire advertisement.

2. Scale the cut.

3. Figure the number of words that would have to be written to occupy the space reserved for text in the layout.

4. Make the finished layout and neatly mark it for the compositor.

Unit 69   SMALL SPACE NEWSPAPER ADVERTISEMENTS

The layout man seldom knows where his advertisement will be placed in a newspaper. Therefore it is necessary for him to have a knowledge of newspaper page make-up.

The inside pages of a newspaper are usually arranged in a step fashion from the right side of the page to the left, (Fig. 1). If an advertisement is three or four columns wide and the full depth of the page, it will undoubtedly be placed to the extreme right. In this case the white margin of the paper will be at the head, foot and right side of the advertisement. It would have to be separated from the other advertisements on the left side, (Fig. 1). Smaller advertisements, of course, would have to be separated on all four sides.

It is difficult for small space advertisements to compete with the large ones. This makes the small space advertisements more difficult to design. Layout men must attract attention to their small advertisement, and then make certain the message can be read at a glance.

Fig. 1

The layout man quite often will resort to dark reverse areas to pull the reader's attention to the small space, (Fig. 2). Another method employed is the use of geometric or unusual shapes, (Fig. 3). At times the copy is placed on an angle in order to make it appear different from the other displays on the page, (Fig. 4).

Considerable thought must be given to the arrangement of the small space advertisement so that it may become the center of interest on the newspaper page.

Fig. 2

Fig. 3

Fig. 4

THE LAYOUT

SMALL SPACE NEWSPAPER ADVERTISEMENT

SIZE: 2 columns by 77 lines (14 agate lines in 1 in.)
DISPLAY HEAD: Sale of Modern Furniture
TEXT: The copy would be written after the layout has been completed, so no definite amount of space has to be reserved for the text.
CUT: 1 1/2 in. by 2 in. deep
SIGNATURE: Brunner, Inc.
10 East 38th St.

DIRECTIONS

1. Make a thumbnail sketch of the small space advertisement.
2. Make the finished layout, marking it for the compositor.

Unit 70   CONTINUITY IN NEWSPAPER LAYOUT

A store or company that advertises regularly in a newspaper should have a style of layout that gives each advertisement a similar arrangement. This continuous appearance of a similar layout format tends to enable the reader to recognize the company or store without reading the signature. This style should be changed from time to time so as not to become tiresome, monotonous and "out of date."

The selection of a distinctive type face, and its use continually will make the advertisement of a store stand apart from the others. The style of layout used is one method employed by some layout men, while others use a certain distinctive style of illustration.

The same border design may be used in every advertisement as a method of creating continuity of style. In some cases the signature of the store may be worked into the border design as in Fig. 1 and Fig. 2.

Fig. 1   Fig. 2

Nearly every company adopts a distinctive signature and uses it continually. This should be changed at times so as to be kept "up to date." If a signature is changed, it should not be a drastic change, but should contain parts that would be easily recognized and associated with the company.

When a store, as a department store, has several advertisements appearing together on one page, each advertisement should be designed as a separate unit. Although they are handled separately the entire arrangement should have a similar layout style so that the reader would easily recognize that they are separate advertisements for one store, (Fig. 3).

Fig. 3

THE LAYOUT
NEWSPAPER ADVERTISEMENT

SIZE: 4 columns by 98 lines deep
DISPLAY HEAD: Unusual Group of Men's Pajamas
TEXT: Don't take our word for this most unusual value. See them for yourself. Every pajama made by one of the largest manufacturers at a price below what we would usually pay. We pass these savings on to you. Choose from broadcloths, percales, stripes, checks and figures.
CUT: 3" x 4" deep
SIGNATURE: Stewart Brothers

DIRECTIONS
1. Make a sketch of the newspaper copy creating a continuity layout style.
2. Copyfit the text and have the instructor check the sketch.
3. Make finished layout marking it for compositor with colored pencil.

Unit 71   HANDLING THE FOLD IN LAYOUT

The handling of two facing pages in layout is difficult because of the fold between the pages. The layout must be so designed that the two pages will appear to belong together, (Fig. 1 and Fig. 2).

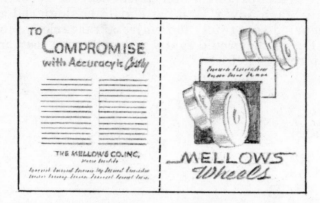

Fig. 1 *Incorrect Appears to be two advertisements... separated by the fold*

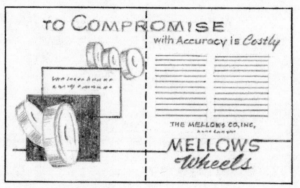

Fig. 2 *Correct. The units are placed so as to appear as one advertisement*

Complete unity of the two pages may be obtained by the use of masses of white space, or by a heading extending partially or completely across the pages, (Fig. 2). Tint blocks, reverse cuts and rules, extending over the fold will aid in tying the two pages together, (Fig. 3), so that the eye will travel smoothly from one page to the other.

Fig. 3 *The use of a reverse cut and a rule to tie the two pages together*

Besides uniting the two pages, the layout man must give some consideration to the placement of illustrations, display lines and type masses, in relation to the fold. A cut should never cross the fold if it is possible to arrange it in any other manner. The fold might pass through an important part of the illustration damaging the appearance of a product displayed or appearing to cut a person in half, (Fig. 4).

Fig. 4 INCORRECT, *The fold passes through the figure in the cut.*

If a cut must cross the fold it should be so arranged that the fold will pass through a section of the illustration that is relatively unimportant, (Fig. 5).

Fig. 5 *The fold passes through an unimportant part of the cut.*

Large display lines may cross the fold without hindering readability, but blocks of 6-, 8-, 10-, 12- and 14-point type should never be arranged so that they are on the fold. The folding of the paper would hinder the readability of the type.

In many cases the designer will camouflage the fold by having the fold on the edge of the illustration, a tint block or rule, (Fig. 6).

Fig. 6 *The layout is arranged so that the fold passes along the edge of the cut.*

When arranging the center spread in folders and broadsides, it is a more difficult feat, as the folds are more numerous and are in different directions. There should be no difficulty as far as appearance and readability is concerned if the spread is handled as one large layout making certain that the folds do not pass through illustrations or blocks of small size type.

―――― THE LAYOUT ――――

TWO PAGE ADVERTISEMENT

SIZE: 12 in. by 8 1/2 in. (Each page
      6 in. by 8 1/2 in. deep)
DISPLAY HEAD: Just look at the difference!
CUT: 2 in. by 1 1/2 in.
CUT: 2 in. by 4 in.
CUT: 3 in. by 2 in.
SUB-HEAD: More miles per gallon
TEXT: No definite amount of space has
      to be reserved for the text.
SIGNATURE: The New Nash Rambler

DIRECTIONS

1. Make a thumbnail sketch of the two page advertisement.

2. Have the instructor check the thumbnail sketch.

3. Make the finished layout.

Unit 72   DESIGNING FOLDERS AND BROADSIDES

DIRECT ADVERTISING

Direct advertising is the type of printed advertising that is given directly to a person by mailing or placing it in the individual's hands by other means. Illustrated letters, announcements, folders, catalogs, booklets, broadsides, envelope and package enclosures are the principle forms of direct advertising literature, and all the rules of good layout are applied to each. The printed piece must be an aid in selling goods or services by attracting attention, creating interest and getting the message read, impressing what it says on the memory of the individual receiving it.

When planning direct advertising, the layout man usually can decide or recommend the quality and color of the paper, the size, shape and fold, the method of reproduction and the color or colors to be used.

FOLDERS AND BROADSIDES

When a printed sheet is folded so that it forms several pages it is called a folder. If a large printed sheet is folded so that when it is opened the center spread is one large display that might be used as a poster, it is called a broadside. Most broadsides are "self-mailers," having a space for the address and stamp on one outside page. Folders are usually mailed in envelopes. One of the most used folders is the one formed by folding a sheet twice at right angles, (Fig. 1). This fold, called the French Fold, is used extensively in the printing of greeting cards and allows the printer to form a four page folder by printing on only one side of the sheet, (Fig. 2).

Fig. 1 – *French Fold*

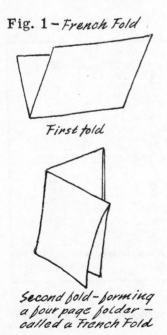

First fold

Second fold-forming a four page folder – called a French Fold

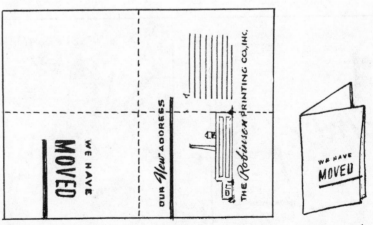

Fig.2- *Four page folder formed by printing on one side of the sheet and using a French Fold*

SIZES OF BROADSIDES AND FOLDERS

The layout man, when designing a folder or broadside must give considerable thought to its size. He must know how it is to be delivered to the individual. If by mail a size will have to be selected that will fit into a standard size envelope. The cost of postage must be considered, so that weight should be checked. To aid in the economy of production, a size should be selected that will cut from a standard size sheet of paper with a minimum of waste.

UNUSUAL FOLDS

The unusual tricky fold is an asset only as long as it attracts attention, increases interest and assists in the carrying of the message. If the fold is quite complicated, the individual may become more interested in the tricky fold than in the printed message.

DESIGNING THE BROADSIDE AND FOLDER

The cover of a broadside or folder is of great importance. It should attract attention and arouse enough interest so that the person receiving it would want to look inside. The design should be appropriate for the article or service advertised, and should appeal to the type of individual it is to be read by. This would determine whether the cover arrangement should be modern or conventional, plain or decorative. Regardless of the method used it must make the reader want to look inside. The cover and inside of a folder should harmonize in every respect, (Fig. 3). The overall arrangement, color and type styles should be similar, or the same.

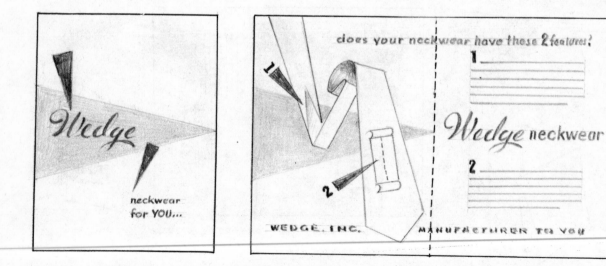

Fig. 3   *The cover and inside of the folder should be similar in design*

─── THE LAYOUT ───

FOUR PAGE FOLDER

SIZE: $3\frac{1}{4}$" x $5\frac{1}{4}$" folder. $6\frac{1}{2}$" x $5\frac{1}{4}$" open.

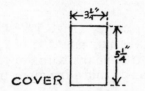
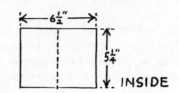

COVER COPY: Will You be Ready?

INSIDE COPY: Are you prepared for the next hurricane?

INSIDE TEXT: It may be next week or next month, or.. it may be tomorrow. You can't prevent it. You can't move your house out of its path. You can insure against the loss resulting from windstorm damage. Get windstorm insurance from The Mutual Insurance Company before the next hurricane strikes.

INSIDE CUT: Cut of a house... $2\frac{1}{2}$" x 2" deep

SIGNATURE: The Mutual Insurance Co.
Boston, Mass.

DIRECTIONS

1. Make a small dummy of the above folder copy and have it checked by the instructor.

2. One color and black may be used.

3. Make the finished layout in the layout pad with the cover design separate from the inside pages.

Unit 73   BOOKLETS

Booklets are printed pieces that are often used in direct advertising. They are small books containing several pages, usually bound together by saddle or side wire stitching. In many cases they are bound by one of the mechanical methods such as plastic or wire bindings.

Booklets usually differ from books in layout style, (Fig. 1). The anatomy of a book is traditional. The order of the pages, margins, position of folios, running heads, etc. in books have followed the same style for years with very little change. Although a booklet resembles a book, the layout man has more freedom in designing it.

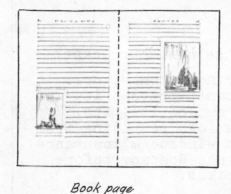 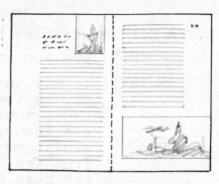

Book page   Fig. 1   *Booklet Page*

A study of the copy by the layout man will guide him in the style of layout. A booklet for a bank would undoubtedly be designed differently than a booklet displaying various car models for an automobile show room. The cover of the booklet should always be well designed, appealing, appropriate and should invite the reader to look inside. The layout man has complete freedom in arranging the inside pages. He may bleed cuts, (Fig. 2), vary margin widths, (Fig. 3), use rules, (Fig. 4) and colored tint blocks. The arrangement of each page will differ because of different size cuts and different copy, but the entire booklet should have a similarity of style or format.

Fig. 2 *The bleeding of cuts utilizes margin space and allows the use of large illustrations.*

192

Fig. 3 *Booklet margins may be arranged in any suit- able manner. They do not have to be arranged in the traditional book style.*

A careful study of all the sales, design and cost factors involved in each job will determine the exact size and shape; whether to bind it on the long or short side, and the kind of binding method to use; whether to use white or colored papers for the cover and text pages; whether to use colored inks; whether to use shapes other than the common rectangular one, whether to use a self-mailer or to plan an envelope mailing.

Before deciding upon the size of a booklet, the designer should check to make certain that it would cut economically from a standard size sheet, with the grain parallel to the fold.

The weight of the paper should be considered. If the booklet has only a few pages, it can be made to appear thicker by using a bulky paper, and if it has many pages, the designer might feel that the paper should be less bulky and lighter in weight. Of course the weight of the finished booklet is important, because of the cost of postage in mailing.

Booklet layout is very interesting. It is a challenge to the layout man because he must apply his knowledge of all the design principles and give thought to many production problems he seldom has to consider in other layout work.

Fig. 4 *Rules may be used in arranging pages in a booklet*

THE LAYOUT

BOOKLET COVER (A)	BOOKLET COVER (B)
SIZE: 4 in. by 8 1/2 in. deep	SIZE: 4 in. by 6 in. deep
COPY: Hotel Mark Hopkins San Francisco Atop Knob Hill	COPY: Introducing Original Designs Jay Thorpe New York
CUT: 2 in. by 3 in. deep	CUT: Small cut of a trade mark

DIRECTIONS

1. Select either copy (A) or (B) and make a thumbnail sketch.

2. One color and black may be used.

2. Make the finished layout in the layout pad with the cover design separate from the inside pages.

Section VI

Applications

The series of problems which follow is designed to give you the opportunity of carrying typical layout jobs through to completion. Not only will you be required to design the layout as directed, applying the principles you have previously studied, but you will carry many of these problems on through the stage of setting the type in the shop and mounting the copy or pulling proofs.

Other than the Directions for each application, the material has been prepared on a conventional typewriter in much the same manner which you will find on the job. Your instructor will direct you in choosing the problems which you are to do.

JOB 1

DIRECTIONS: (a) Arrange the following business card copy, using type that is available in the printing department.
  (b) Mark-up the layout and have it checked by the instructor.
  (c) Set the layout in the shop and pull a neat reproduction proof.
  (d) Mount the layout and proof on an 8 1/2″ × 11″ sheet of index bristol.

SIZE: $4\frac{1}{2}$″ x $2\frac{1}{2}$″

COPY: Charles A. Lawes, Inc.
Creative Printers
626 Federal Street
Chicago, Illinois

G. J. Roberts

JOB 2

DIRECTIONS: Design, mark-up, set-up and mount the following copy.

MAGAZINE ADVERTISEMENT

SIZE: 3″ x 5″

DISPLAY HEAD: Good Copy

TEXT: Good copy goes further than a hard persistent attempt to push goods on a preoccupied public. While its purpose is to sell, it can also suggest ideas to the benefit of everyone concerned.

SIGNATURE: Harvey, Inc.
Advertising

JOB 3

DIRECTIONS: (a) Design, mark-up, set-up and mount the following copy.
(b) One color and black may be used, and a cut suggested.

COVER

SIZE: 4" x 6"

COPY: Is there a TENOR in the house?

JOB 4

DIRECTIONS: (a) Design, mark-up, set-up and mount the following copy.
(b) One color and black may be used.

SHIPPING LABEL

SIZE: 5" x 3"

COPY: The Lakeside Press
R. L. Donaldson Company
350 East Main Street
Cleveland, Ohio

JOB 5

DIRECTIONS: (a) Design, mark-up, set-up and mount the following copy.
(b) You may use one or two colors and black.
(c) A cut or tint block may be suggested or used.

PROGRAM COVER

SIZE: 4" x 6"

COPY: Program
Fall Meeting
Graphic Arts Club

JOB 6

DIRECTIONS: (a) Design, mark-up, set-up and mount the following.
               (b) One color and black may be used.
               (c) A cut or tint block may be used.

BLOTTER

SIZE: 7" x 3½"

DISPLAY HEAD: First Impressions

TEXT: Before the words of an advertisement are read, the reader sees mere blocks of type. If that first visual impression does not intrigue him, he may never read those words you have so carefully chosen. Good typography by skillful interpretation tries to sell him before he reads.

SIGNATURE: The Hall Printing Company
                   Hartford, Connecticut

JOB 7

DIRECTIONS: (a) Design, mark-up, set-up and mount the following.
               (b) One color and black may be used.
               (c) A cut may be used if desired.

ANNOUNCEMENT CARD

SIZE: 5½" x 3¼"

COPY: Announcing

We are pleased to inform the friends of Mr. Donald M. Havens that he has become a member of our staff in the interior decorating studios. Third floor.

SIGNATURE: The Baliff Company

JOB 8

DIRECTIONS: (a) Design, mark-up, set-up and mount the following copy.
(b) Black ink only.

NEWSPAPER ADVERTISEMENT

SIZE: 3 columns by 140 lines

DISPLAY HEAD: Velvety Evening Gowns

TEXT: Full bell skirt beneath a snug bodice. Beautifully shaped low neckline, made flattering by a touch of snowy white rayon. Silk or rayon velvet, in blue, red or winter night black. Sizes 12 to 20. Proud, lovely lines with small flowers that give a touch of beauty, and mark the delightful pockets.

$29.95 in the Specialty Shop

CUT: Use a cut of a girl posed in a gown. Any size may be used.

SIGNATURE: Bonwit Teller

JOB 9

DIRECTIONS: (a) Design, set and mount the following copy.
(b) One color and black may be used.
(c) A cut may be used if desired.

FOLDER

SIZE: You may select the size and type of fold you wish to use

COVER COPY: Don't Gamble

INSIDE COPY: Do you gamble with your business? Maybe... just maybe...you will get some business by sitting around and waiting for it. On the other hand a good many of your competitors are going out after business. Why sit back and let the other fellow attract all of the attention? Tell your story by means of smart up-to-minute printing. That is where we can help you. Use printing to tell them and sell them.

SIGNATURE: True Printing Co., Dayton, Ohio

JOB 10

DIRECTIONS: (a) Design, set and mount the following copy.
(b) One color and black may be used.
(c) A cut or tint block may be used if desired.

ADVERTISING CARD

SIZE: $3\frac{1}{2}$" x $5\frac{1}{2}$"

HEAD: Bulls-eye

TEXT: Some printing goes straight to the mark, looks brisk, clean cut, stimulating. That's the kind of printing we do. We are ready at the drop of a hat to prove our claims. Let us show specimens and ways we can serve you. Phone Main 1939.

SIGNATURE: The Thompson Co.
10 Main St.,
Atlanta, Georgia

JOB 11

DIRECTIONS: (a) Design, set and mount the following job.
(b) Color and cuts may be used.

LETTERHEAD

SIZE: $8\frac{1}{2}$" x 11"

COPY: VanCamp and Best Co.
Vanco Stainless Steel
Bethlehem, Pennsylvania

JOB 12

DIRECTIONS: (a) Design, set and mount the following job.
(b) Color and cuts may be used.
SHIPPING LABEL

SIZE: 5" x 2 3/4"

COPY: Ace Printing Company
Hartford, Connecticut

To _____

_____

JOB 13

DIRECTIONS: (a) Design, set and mount the following.
(b) A cut, any size desired, may be used.

NEWSPAPER ADVERTISEMENT

SIZE: 2 col. by 140 lines

HEAD: A HAT for Young Men

TEXT: The graceful sweep and dip of the fall creations
in our young men's hats set them apart from the
rank and file. They were designed exclusively for
us by Burt-Mayer, leading stylists to young men.

Reasonably priced
$10.00

SIGNATURE: Kable-Eddy Shop
Hotel Bateson
Detroit, Michigan

JOB 14

DIRECTIONS: (a) Design, set and mount the following.
(b) Black and one color may be used.

BILLHEAD

SIZE: 8½" x 5½"

COPY: Reise Printing Company
134 James Street
Brooklyn, N.Y.

Sold To _____

_____

_____

JOB 15

DIRECTIONS: (a) Design, set and mount the following.
               (b) One color and black may be used.
               (c) A cut or tint block may be used if desired.

SIZE: 3" x 5" folded

COVER COPY: Who Pays?

INSIDE HEAD: New Business pays the Cost

INSIDE TEXT: Whenever direct mail salesmanship is effective, the value of the new business it creates always exceeds the cost of going after it. Successful advertising pays for itself.

SIGNATURE: E. C. ROWE PRINTING COMPANY
                 New Haven,
                 Connecticut

JOB 16

DIRECTIONS: (a) Design, set and mount the following.
               (b) A cut may be used if desired.

MAGAZINE ADVERTISEMENT

SIZE: 2 col. by 70 lines

HEAD: Refinancing

TEXT: The home owner often meets the problem of renewing a maturing mortgage and in many instances is compelled to secure a new loan elsewhere. If problems like this arise, we will help you solve them.

SIGNATURE: Security Investment Company
                New York Avenue, Newark, N. J.